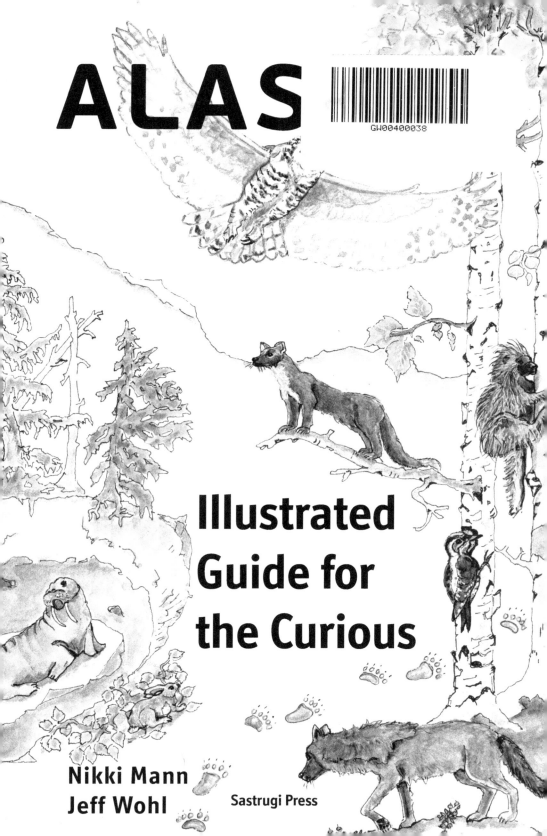

ALAS

Illustrated Guide for the Curious

Nikki Mann
Jeff Wohl

Sastrugi Press

Sastrugi Press / Published by arrangement with the author

Alaska: Illustrated Guide for the Curious

The authors have made every effort to accurately describe the locations contained in this work. Travel to some locations in this book is hazardous. The publisher has no control over and does not assume any responsibility for author or third-party websites or their content describing these locations, how to travel there, nor how to do it safely. Refer to local regulations and laws.

Any person exploring these locations is personally responsible for checking local conditions prior to departure. You are responsible for your own actions and decisions. The information contained in this work is based solely on the author's research at the time of publication and may not be accurate in the future. Neither the publisher nor the author assumes any liability for anyone climbing, exploring, visiting, or traveling to the locations described in this work. Climbing is dangerous by its nature. Any person engaging in mountain climbing is responsible for learning the proper techniques. The reader assumes all risks and accepts full responsibility for injuries, including death.

Sastrugi Press
PO Box 1297, Jackson, WY 83001, United States
www.sastrugipress.com
Quantity sales: Special discounts are available on quantity purchases by corporations, associations, and others. For details, contact the publisher at the address above.

Library of Congress Catalog-in-Publication Data
Library of Congress Control Number: 2019933169
Mann, Nikki and Wohl, Jeff
Alaska / Nikki Mann, Jeff Wohl -1st United States edition
p. cm.
1. Nature 2. Alaska 3. Wildlife 4. Biology
Summary: Learn interesting information about Alaska's Natural History including: animal tracking, bear safety, birds, marine life, plants, and ecological processes.

ISBN-13: 978-1-944986-59-9 (hardback), 978-1-944986-58-2 (paperback)

508.4—dc23

Printed in the United States of America when purchased in the United States

All photography, maps, illustrations, and artwork by the authors, except as noted.

10 9 8 7 6 5 4 3 2 1

Table of Contents

Awaken Your
Curiosity

There are no special tools. You don't need a degree or intensive training. You don't have to carry anything extra. All you need is your curiosity. Ask questions. Look harder. Find answers. Find correlations. Get interested. Buy more guide books. Go on more cruises, or backpacking trips, or sit outside in a comfortable chair. Always keep your sense of wonder and excitement.

This book isn't a textbook or an all-encompassing guide to the vastness and magic of Alaska. It's a start—a solid poking under the leaves, a sniff of a strange musky odor, the tang of an almost-ripe berry, a peek through the binoculars into a world you might not be familiar with.

The authors have watched, tracked, and even raised some of these species. They have collected and sifted the careful research and observations of many fantastic scientists, naturalists, and teachers, some of whom they've had the honor of working with and learning from.

Moose are huge and well adapted to living in snow with long legs and special gut bacteria to digest tree cambium (inner bark).

There is a list of these people at the end of this book. You are encouraged to check out their books and resources. There is a whole world of discovery waiting in those pages.

For now, let's go wandering with our eyes, ears, nose, and tasters ready. Sling your curiosity over your shoulder or on your hip belt, wherever it best fits, and head out. After all, this is Alaska.

There is
adventure
everywhere!

Hoary marmots, like many other rodents, eat the specialized type of bone called antlers for the calcium they contain.

Can you find all the...
Bear Signs

Hint: 11

Bears love to **make their own marks** on trail signs. Look for bite marks, claw scratches, and even hairs that leave information for the next bears who come along.

 Tracks are great indicators of bear activity, especially if you know the previous weather and can guess how old they are.

 Ants are wonderful bear food. Bears tear into mounds but usually leave enough ants for the colony to survive so they can be raided again later.

Ground squirrels standing up and making loud calls are good indicators that bears are around, or have recently been there. Bears will dig squirrels out of their holes.

Old logs contain lots of ants and grubs, which bears tear apart to get at the tasty meal.

 **Cow parsnip** might cause skin reactions in some unfortunate people, but bears find them quite tasty, eating the entire plant or just the tops.

Devil's club might be mildly toxic to people but bears like the berries. They usually take only the tops, but since their long claws are not particularly dexterous, they eat the berries, stem, and all.

 Insects under rocks are tasty bear food. Bears **flip rocks** over to scoop up dinner. Lichens on the underside of rocks are a good indication of a flipped rock.

 Berry bushes, like Highbush cranberry, that look like they've been trashed by a mini tornado, are a good sign of a bear picking berries.

 The fifth claw does not always show in **tree climbs**. Up climb marks will often be small, clear scratches. When they come down, bears slide and leave long gouges. Bear cubs climb for protection. Black bears also climb for food.

 Fish are a great protein for bears, but during spawning season when fish are abundant, bears get picky. They eat just a bite or only eggs.

5

Learning bear behavior is fascinating and can keep you safe. Can you figure out what's going on here? Try to guess the story for each bear scenario. How might you respond to keep both you and the bear safe and observe amazing behavior?

1 A **charging bear** is when you need to have your bear spray in your hand and probably already deployed! Don't run. Hold your arms over your head to look bigger than you are. There are lots of reasons bears might charge but the most common is when they are surprised or to protect cubs or food. You can prevent surprise interaction by making noise as you travel. Some people do this with bells.

2 When you see **bear tracks**, if they are fresh, look carefully for little prints as well. Also, be sure to look up nearby trees if a bear seems to be guarding something. If you are hiking with your dog, keep them nearby so they don't irritate the bear and bring the bear to you.

3 When a **bear stands** on their hind legs they look very impressive but don't assume this is aggression. A bear's sense of smell is approx. 2,100 times better than ours! They often stand up, especially when in thick bushes, to get a better sniff, or to get the best view with their relatively small eyes. This is a good time to let them know you are there with a, "Hey Bear! Hey Bear!"

Some things **you** should know about

Bear Safety

BEAR SPRAY

1

Bear spray can create a cloud of atomized pepper spray up to 30 feet away from you. The bear will walk or run into this cloud, causing them to temporarily lose sight and smell. Bear spray is ideally deployed on a charging bear before they get to you.

4 Bears are very intelligent and learn quickly when they get **food rewards**. Improperly stored food is one of the most unfortunate ways to create a bad human-bear interaction. Always store your food somewhere safe, in an approved bear box or canister, or hung in a tree. NEVER approach a bear guarding food! If you see or smell something dead, pull your bear spray and back away.

SPRAY

Always keep spray accessible, on a holster on your belt or in your hand. Quick draw is essential! One per person is best. Try to position yourself upwind of any bear making you nervous, but if you can't or don't have time, deploy bear spray even if the wind is coming at you.

TIPS Bear spray teaches bears to respect people and keep their distance, whereas guns only make dead bears or orphan cubs who often grow up to cause more trouble. Bear spray is worth every penny.

Bear Hang

10 feet off the ground
4 feet from the trunk
4 feet below the limb

Bear Behavior

Tracks, Sign and Telling Stories

Gait Patterns

Transverse gallop = long distance between sets. In a canter or gallop, hinds come through and land further forward than the front feet.

Roto-gallop makes a "C" shape pattern. Hunting or escape speed.

Diamonds= Hinds and Circles = Fronts

Tracking is so much more than looking at a print in the mud or snow. It is looking at claw marks on trees, rodent tunnels through the grass, and ground squirrel poop under rocks. Tracking can make you feel like a wilderness Jedi.

Always look for animal sign. There is not a square meter in the wild without animal sign. It might be the hair of a squirrel or the scat of a shrew, but it is there.

If you look hard enough, you can see where squirrels have run and jumped off logs, where caribou have lain in the tundra grass, where the mice have been cleaning up your scraps. Each track has a story; you just need to find it! Never pass a muddy patch without looking for tracks.

Polar Bear Track: Approx. size of average adult front right (bears, unlike humans, have small toe on the inside)

When you find a sign, ask these **five** questions:

Who made the mark?
Male or female? Young or old?

What were they doing?
Trotting, walking, bounding (relaxed or stressed)?

Where were they going?
Uphill? Downhill? North? South?

When? How long ago?
How has the weather affected the tracks?

Why? To safety? To food? To water?
Away from us? Try to act out the scene.
It's hard, but it will provide great insight.

The gait patterns on the sides of these pages are standard for most four-legged animals: cats, dogs, caribou, and even bear, although bears are very pigeon-toed (toes pointing inward). Gait patterns are a great way to see the "story" left by the tracks, not just identify the individual print. Remember in fast travel, the hind feet pass the front feet. Also, hind feet are usually smaller than fronts because they carry less weight (except bears).

Gait Patterns

Trot is like walk except more distance between prints. Also baseline.

Walk is baseline gate; animal at ease. Hinds can be directly on top of fronts, before, after or off to side.

Diamonds= Hinds
Circles = Fronts

Bounding Hare

Bear Family

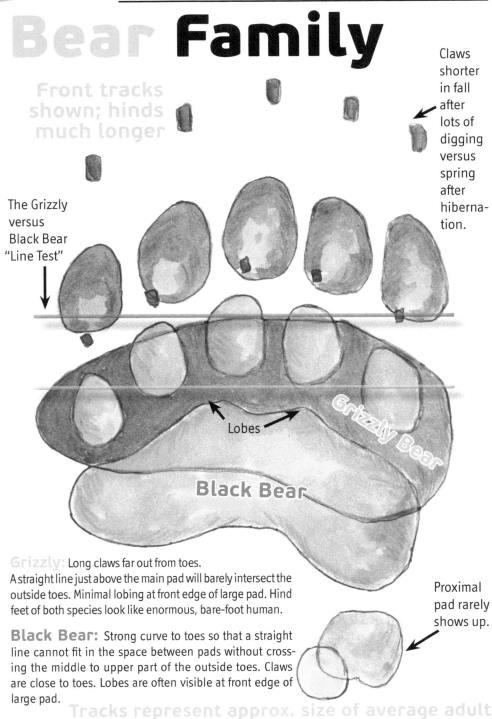

Front tracks shown; hinds much longer

Claws shorter in fall after lots of digging versus spring after hibernation.

The Grizzly versus Black Bear "Line Test"

Lobes

Grizzly Bear

Black Bear

Grizzly: Long claws far out from toes.
A straight line just above the main pad will barely intersect the outside toes. Minimal lobing at front edge of large pad. Hind feet of both species look like enormous, bare-foot human.

Black Bear: Strong curve to toes so that a straight line cannot fit in the space between pads without crossing the middle to upper part of the outside toes. Claws are close to toes. Lobes are often visible at front edge of large pad.

Proximal pad rarely shows up.

Tracks represent approx. size of average adult

Polar Bears split from Brown bears around 150,000 years ago when they remained in snow-covered habitats and began swimming in the ocean to hunt seals and other marine mammals. They have huge feet for paddling and short, sharp claws as ice crampons.

Brown Bears, also known as Grizzly Bears, have massive shoulders for digging, a dished face, and long claws for tearing up soil to get roots and insects. They are often brown to blonde.

Polar Bear
avg. 700-1500 pounds (lbs)

Shoulder hump

Brown Bear/ Grizzly
avg. 600-1300 lbs

Black Bear
avg. 200-500 lbs

Black Bears have big, cute ears, flat faces, and relatively short claws which allow them to climb trees for both safety and to eat nutritious tree buds. They can be, and are, eaten by Brown bears if they don't get out of the way. They can be an identical color to Brown bears, which makes looking for the Brown bear shoulder hump, dish-face with small ears, and long claws important to tell the two species apart. Brown bears are more likely to be aggressive towards humans, so identifying the difference between the two species is important.

11

Dog Family

Tracks represent approx. size of average adult

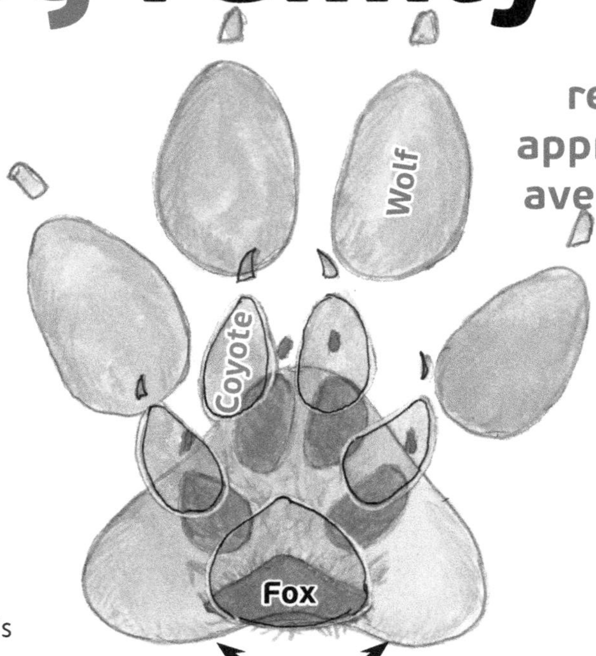

Wolf

Coyote

Fox

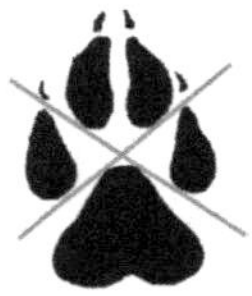

Dog tracks are longer than wide with dull claws showing.

Dog tracks fit "X" shape between pads

Bi-lobing (2 bulges) on back of main pad

Cat Family

Look for "Leading Toe" (one toe in front of rest, not usually present in dogs)

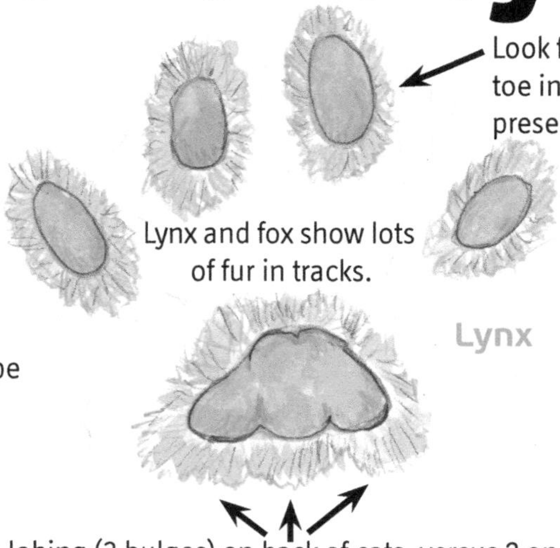

Lynx and fox show lots of fur in tracks.

Cat track is round in shape with sharp claws hidden

Lynx

Cat tracks only fit an "H" shape between pads, not "X" of dogs

Tri-lobing (3 bulges) on back of cats, versus 2 on dog.

Coyotes, like wolves, often live in family packs and spend time yipping and yowling as a group. They are very opportunistic hunters and eat everything from insects to berries to mammals.

Coyote
1.9-2.2 feet at shoulder, 22-30 lbs

Gray Wolf
2.2-2.7 feet at shoulder
80-115 lbs

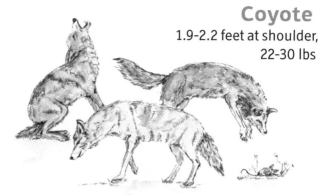

Wolves who hung around early humans and began to cooperate with them are the ancestors of all domestic dogs, *Canis familiaris*.

Canada Lynx
1.6-1.8 feet at shoulder
18-24 lbs

Canada lynx are a cat with the body the size of a medium-small, extra-fuzzy dog, but the paws of a mountain lion! They need these snowshoes for staying on top to hunt hares in deep winter drifts.

Red Fox
1.2-1.7 feet at shoulder
6-15 lbs

Arctic Fox
0.8-1 feet
6-10 lbs

Red fox (left) are larger and heavier than the Arctic fox in white winter coat (right). Foxes are very curious, sometimes even towards people.

Weasel Family

Wolverine

Proximal pad
on wolverine
may show.

Diamonds = Hinds
Circles = Fronts

River Otter

Mink

Otter and mink
have webbed
toes for
swimming.

These tracks appear to be
in "3s" especially in snow.
Indicates wolverine.

Weasel: This family always has five toes in the front and hind
(unlike the rodent family which has 4 in front and 5 in the hind).
However, the fifth toe is small and doesn't always show up. Other
weasel tracks you might see are: Pine marten, Long and Short-
tailed weasel, and Sea otter.

Tracks represent approx. size of average adult

The wolverine, like most weasels, is incredibly ferocious and will very occasionally tackle prey hugely disproportionate to its size, like moose in deep snow. They also have been known to regularly climb thousands of feet of near-vertical snow when there was an easy way around. Perhaps they do it just because they can.

Note: we are measuring weasels in length rather than shoulder height as that is their most notable size characteristic.

Wolverine
2.8-3.25 feet
in length
15-45 lbs

Northern River Otter

3.7-5 feet
in length
including
long tail
15-35 lbs

River otters can use their webbed feet to swim 20 mph, which helps in catching fish and traveling to find crustaceans. They are incredibly playful and often travel in family groups.

Mink
1.6-2 feet in length
3-5 lbs

Mink are semi-aquatic weasels that spend much of their time hunting for fish, snakes, small mammals and birds. However, they will also tackle muskrats, which are three times their size. That would be like us trying to hunt a Black bear using only our teeth!

15

Ungulates

Tracks represent approx. size of average adult

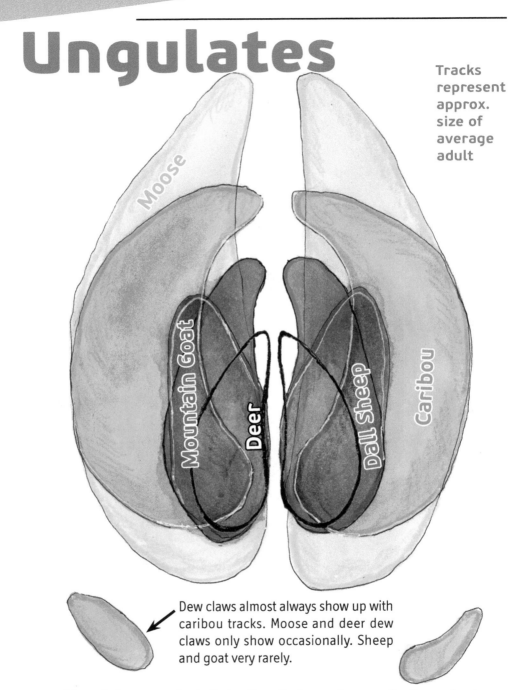

Moose

Mountain Goat

Deer

Dall Sheep

Caribou

Dew claws almost always show up with caribou tracks. Moose and deer dew claws only show occasionally. Sheep and goat very rarely.

Ungulates are animals that walk on their ungules, or nails. Remember to look at location when identifying tracks. You are unlikely to see Mountain goat tracks (the rock climbers) where moose live (wetland dwellers).

Mountain Goat

2.75-3 feet
at shoulder
140-280 lbs

Dall Sheep

3-3.5 feet
at shoulder
150-300 lbs

Mountain goats can fit all four feet onto a two inch by six inch rock. The pads of their hooves are similar to the sticky rubber of climbing shoes for extra grip.

Dall sheep are high angle specialists, and ram horns together at incredible speeds.

Moose

4.6-7 feet
at shoulder
800-1500 lbs

Moose are often found in willows or other shrubs in summer, and in the winter eating spruce tree tips or aspen bark. Their antlers can be over 60 inches wide and, unlike horns, are shed every year.

Caribou grow the largest antlers in relation to body size of any deer species. Male caribou antlers can reach 53 inches tall.

Caribou

3-5 feet
at shoulder
300-400 lbs

Sitka Deer

1.7-3.6 feet at shoulder
80-120 lbs

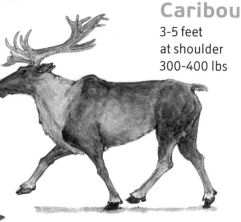

Sitka Black-tailed deer are heavily reliant on uneven-age, old-growth spruce and hemlock forests for winter survival.

17

Rodent and Hare

Note: Four toes on fronts; five on hinds
Tracks represent approxi-
mate size of average adult

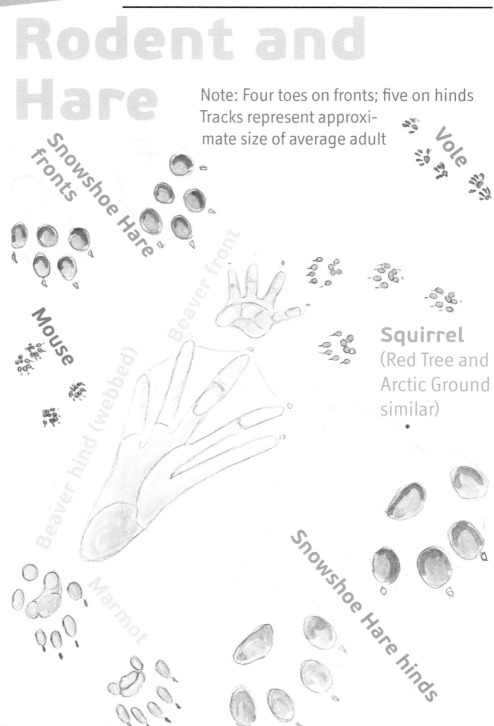

Vole

Snowshoe Hare fronts

Beaver front

Beaver hind (webbed)

Mouse

Squirrel
(Red Tree and
Arctic Ground
similar)

Marmot

Snowshoe Hare hinds

Getting to the Bones of it

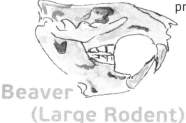

Small Rodent

Rabbit

Beaver (Large Rodent)

Pocket gophers (rodents) have very small eyes since they aren't useful for underground life, hence their skulls have small eye sockets.

Rabbits have two sets of upper incisors and holes in the bones near their sinuses.

Beaver have very impressive wood chisels for teeth. The orange/red pigment on the teeth is iron oxide, which helps strengthen and protect them.

Weasel

Dog Family

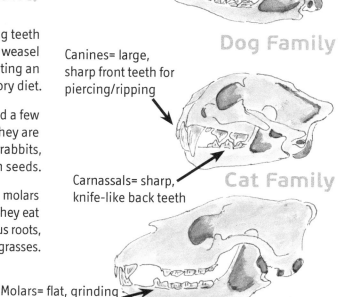

Notice the severe ripping teeth (carnassals) on the weasel and cat skull, indicating an exclusively predatory diet.

Dogs have rippers and a few grinding molars. They are opportunistic, eating rabbits, berries, and even seeds.

Bears have a lot of grinding molars for an omnivorous diet. They eat meat, but also lost of fibrous roots, plants, and even grasses.

Canines= large, sharp front teeth for piercing/ripping

Carnassals= sharp, knife-like back teeth

Cat Family

Molars= flat, grinding back teeth

Bear

Predator and

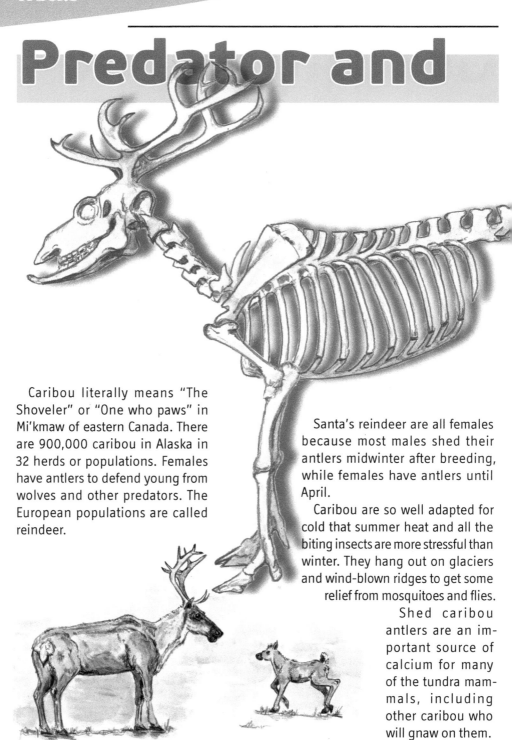

Caribou literally means "The Shoveler" or "One who paws" in Mi'kmaw of eastern Canada. There are 900,000 caribou in Alaska in 32 herds or populations. Females have antlers to defend young from wolves and other predators. The European populations are called reindeer.

Santa's reindeer are all females because most males shed their antlers midwinter after breeding, while females have antlers until April.

Caribou are so well adapted for cold that summer heat and all the biting insects are more stressful than winter. They hang out on glaciers and wind-blown ridges to get some relief from mosquitoes and flies.

Shed caribou antlers are an important source of calcium for many of the tundra mammals, including other caribou who will gnaw on them.

Red foxes come in color morphs other than red, the most common being a "silver" morph (appears black). From a distance, they have the color appearance of wolves.

Prey

There are estimated to be over 10,000 wolves in Alaska. Adults can weigh up to 150 pounds. Caribou is a favorite prey for interior wolves, but wolves will eat mice and even spawning salmon. They are one of the top predators in Alaska, playing a "keystone" role for the entire ecosystem. Wolves are very social and will even play and cooperate with ravens to find prey.

Wolves have an intricate and complicated social structure. Researchers in Yellowstone have estimated that two-thirds of all wolf mortality is caused by other wolves. They looked at what made a pack more likely to survive a confrontation with another pack.

As expected, having more wolves made a huge difference. A pack with six versus five wolves more than doubled their chances of survival, but even better than that was having an old wolf. That's right. Respect your elders. This surprised researchers, who thought wolves in fighting prime would be more valuable, but not so. Experience and hard-earned wisdom was the single biggest factor in a wolf packs' success.

Bird Language

Birds are the biggest gossips. They just can't stop talking about everything around them. Caribou, squirrels, rabbits, coyotes and many other mammals listen to whether the birds are relaxed or alarmed. If you learn the different voices of the birds, you too can find an owl hidden from view in the top of a tree, spot a lynx hunting a half-mile away, or avoid bumping into a bear. We know it sounds far-fetched, but it works!

STEP 1

Spend Time Watching

This requires quiet patience. Fortunately, you are in a beautiful, wild place—the perfect place to get to know some birds. The more you know about a bird, watching them when they are relaxed, the easier it will be to notice when they are upset or vigilant. Tune those ears!

Stellar's jays, like most Corvid species, are smart, curious, and very loud. They are good at spotting owls, cats, and other predators. Unfortunately, these jays can be a tough read, as they are loud all the time.

STEP 2

Learn the five "voices" of the birds. Four of these voices are "base-line behaviors" and one is an alarm.

Song: melodic and defends a territory; also attracts a mate.

Companion Calls: soft "chips" and "pips", often while feeding.

Juvenile Begging: loud, wanting to be fed.

Male-to-Male Aggression: sounds like an alarm, but all other birds do not pay attention.

Alarm: many different alarms exist, some for aerial predators, some for ground predators. Sometimes the alarm is nonvocal, as birds fly to cover as fast as they can. Sometimes the birds are screaming, and sometimes they are just silent! You know you have heard this when you have said, "It's almost creepy quiet."

STEP 3

When something changes in bird behavior, ask "Why?"
Practice! Practice! Find a quiet spot to watch and listen, and really learn your birds. Listen to squirrels and other small prey species, too!

Falcons: Long, narrow wings; eats other birds, rodents, and insects. Gryfalcon (shown), American kestrel and peregrine possible.

Eagles: Very broad and long wings with "fingers" often visible at tips. Eats medium-size mammals (marmots "cheep" a warning) and carrion. Bald eagles also fish. Juvenile Golden eagle shown.

Common raven: They often look like a raptor. Look for wedge-shaped tail.

R
A
P
T
O
R

S
H
A
P
E
S

Osprey: Long, very thin wings often bent. Only eats fish.

Harrier (male shown): Long, narrow wings with fingers for soaring over open country hunting small mammals.

Accipiters: Short, rounded wings, long tail for maneuverability hunting other birds in forested areas. Large Sharp-shinned hawk (shown). Goshawk possible. These hunters cause the most dramatic bird alarms.

Buteo: (In Middle) Broad, short wings for soaring and hunting in the open for rabbits, squirrels, snakes and carrion. Rough-legged hawk shown. Red-tailed hawk possible.

23

Bird Language

Tune your ears to what the birds and other very vocal prey species, like squirrels, are telling you. This language is not only amazing for seeing exciting animal species but can also be a great tool for staying safer in bear country. It takes practice, asking questions, and always being curious.

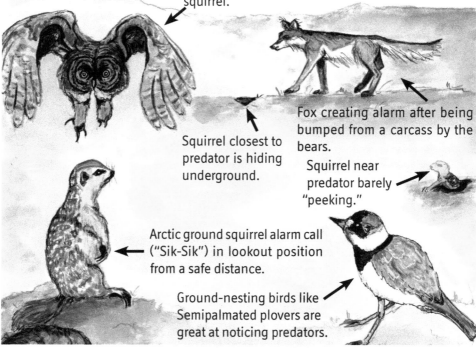

Use vistas to take a moment and scan the landscape, not only for activity, but also for potential blind spots (like thick willows) you might be traveling through.

Bald eagles may fish, but they are also great scavengers and can indicate current or future bear activity.

Great Gray owl "wake hunting," taking advantage of distraction created by the fox to sneak up on a ground squirrel.

Fox creating alarm after being bumped from a carcass by the bears.

Squirrel closest to predator is hiding underground.

Squirrel near predator barely "peeking."

Arctic ground squirrel alarm call ("Sik-Sik") in lookout position from a safe distance.

Ground-nesting birds like Semipalmated plovers are great at noticing predators.

Predators impact their environment like a stone thrown into a pond. Even if you don't see the stone land, sometimes you can track the stone back by following the ripples. Predators such as bears, cats and raptors create their own ripples in the prey around them. The most agitated alarms are the closest to the source (although remember this can be silence because they don't want to be eaten).

and Bear Safety

Scavengers like ravens hang around for scraps after the bear leaves.

Common merganser ducks flying off the river after a Grizzly arrives.

Bears in dense willow thickets can be easy to surprise, but they themselves have surprised and alarmed birds and squirrels along the way. Look and listen for them.

Alarm birds, like White-crowned sparrows, hop to the top of shrubs on "lookout" and give alarm calls.

Black-capped chickadee adding more "dees" to his alarm call.

Birds of a Feather

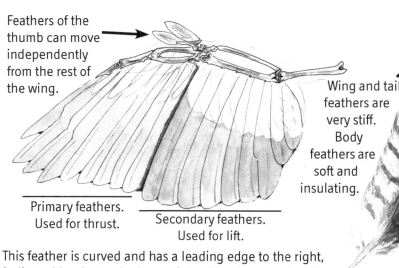

Feathers of the thumb can move independently from the rest of the wing.

Primary feathers. Used for thrust.

Secondary feathers. Used for lift.

Wing and tail feathers are very stiff. Body feathers are soft and insulating.

Dark pigment is physically stronger than light pigment, which is why wingtips are often darker than the rest of the wing.

This feather is curved and has a leading edge to the right, indicated by shorter barbs on right side of a curved quill. This indicates it could be a wing feather.

Example Feather: Red-tailed hawk

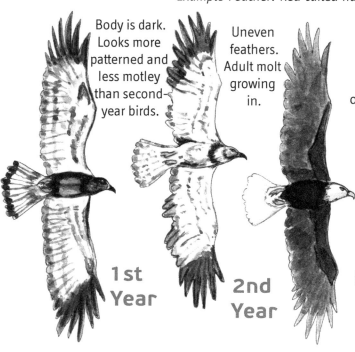

Body is dark. Looks more patterned and less motley than second-year birds.

Uneven feathers. Adult molt growing in.

Birds molt, or drop, all feathers at least once a year (most birds do this twice a year). Juvenile birds often have very different plumage than adults. Males also often have different plumage than females.

1st Year

2nd Year

Mature Bald Eagle

Bird bones are not solid but a honeycomb-like structure with air pockets for decreased weight. This is an essential adaptation for flight.

Spring
Breeding
Plumage

Willow ptarmigan are a large, ground-nesting Alaska resident. Since they do not migrate, they have amazing cold and winter adaptations, which include incredible camouflage abilities. In winter they are pure white to match snow, but for spring and fall they only molt some feathers to blend into snow patches and brown vegetation.

Fall

Winter

Summer

Sketch It

What color is a robin's beak?

| Start with basic shapes: circles, triangles and lines. | Connect them to form rough shape of bird and color delineations. | The American robin and Varied thrush have similar body shape but different markings. |

Common

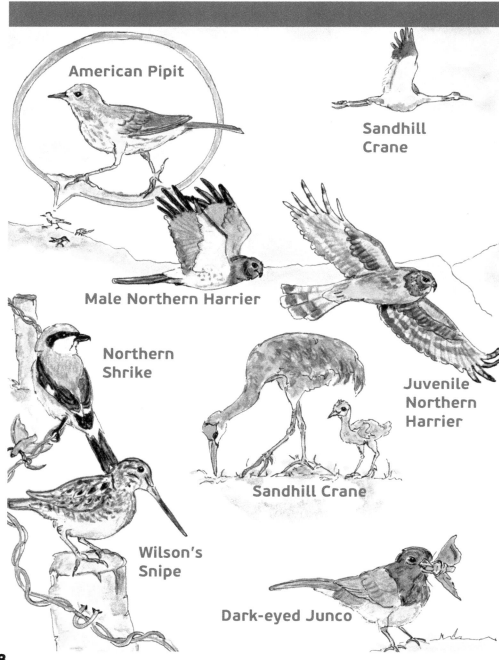

American Pipit

Sandhill Crane

Male Northern Harrier

Northern Shrike

Juvenile Northern Harrier

Sandhill Crane

Wilson's Snipe

Dark-eyed Junco

Birds

Great Blue Heron

Red-breasted Nuthatch

Black-billed Magpie

Hairy Woodpecker

Yellow-rumped Warbler

Belted Kingfisher

Great Blue Heron

Goldeneye

Ruby-crowned Kinglet

Hermit Thrush

Wilson's Phalarope

Beyond Names

Black-billed magpies have stunning, iridescent feathers. Like all members of the Corvid family, they are incredibly smart and very social. They feed on a lot of carrion, which makes them great indicators to look for bear activity.

Male **Northern harriers** are sleek gray, and like most raptors (birds who hunt other birds or mammals), are much smaller than their female mates. They tip back and forth as they glide low over the land, hunting rodents and rabbits.

Juvenile **Northern harriers** have a disk of feathers around their face that makes them look like owls. Females have a brown plumage, or feather color.

Sandhill cranes are elegant dancers, amazing flying singers (with their necks stretched out) and can be seen in fields and meadows feeding. They are as opportunistic as they come, eating seeds, berries, leaves, invertebrates and small mammals.

Dark-eyed juncos feed primarily on the ground, which makes them great lookouts. They will tell other birds when both aerial predators and ground predators are around.

American pipits nest on the ground in the tundra and spend much of their time in small flocks, walking to feed and wagging their tails as they go.

Northern shrikes have mastered the toasting fork, except they use the sun instead of fire. They impale their prey, often lizards, insects, or small mammals, on wire or sticks to dehydrate. Jerky anyone?

There really is a **snipe**! They have a long bill for probing into mud to find tasty treats. Males can be heard winnowing (a wo wo wo wo wo wo wo waa) as they dive down toward their meadow, letting the air whistle through pairs of stiff, outer tail feathers.

Great Blue herons have spear-fishing bills. They hunt primarily fish and frogs. They fly with their necks tucked in.

Hermit thrushes are the secret singers of the trees. Their song sounds like a haunting glass flute.

Goldeneye ducks have bright, golden eyes and beaks with sharp hooks and teeth for eating small fish. Brown females blend into their nests.

If you see a **Wilson's phalarope**, it will probably be in shallow water spinning circles until you're dizzy watching it. They are pushing around with their feet, creating a vortex in the water to pull up small bits of food. Then they open and close their bill many times, using the natural bond of water molecules to each other to suck the water up their bill. They practice gender equity. The smaller, duller males sit on the nest while the big, flashy females protect and defend.

Belted kingfishers perch high and dive into water to catch their fish. Females have two belts, one blue around their neck and one red across their chest. Males only have blue one.

Ruby-crowned kinglets are the ultimate fidgets, flitting from place to place, wings flicking upward. The ruby head feathers are rarely visible.

Yellow-rumped warblers have a convenient yellow rump patch. They are talented insect eaters, and like forested or shrubby areas.

Red-breasted nuthatches love going down the tree head-first, using their stout bills to probe under bark for insects and spiders. They call "nut...nut...nut" in a raspy, repetitive tone.

Hairy woodpeckers, like all woodpeckers, have cushioned brains for drilling their beaks into wood for food and shelter. They have stiff tail feathers they use like a third leg, propping them against the tree. Their toes are two forward, two back, making for great grip on vertical surfaces.

Beach Creatures

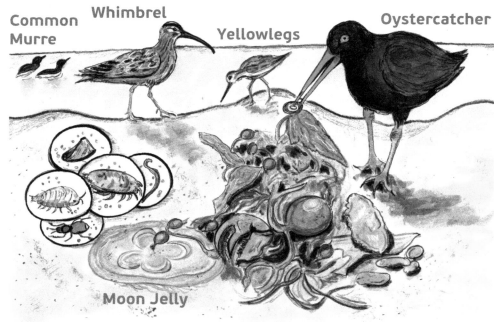

Common Murre · Whimbrel · Yellowlegs · Oystercatcher · Moon Jelly

Beach Wrack

Beach wrack, or washed-up debris (seaweed, wood, crab parts, jellyfish, carcasses) are a whole ecosystem to themselves and support invertebrates which are eaten by shorebirds and mammals.

Shell Critters: *This includes snails eating decomposing seaweeds or clams buried in the mud, filter-feeding around wrack.*

Isopods: *Rollie Polies of the sea. They only live in the sand, cannot move very far, and are very susceptible to vehicles and beach disturbance.*

Sand Crabs: *These egg-shaped creatures follow the tides to remain shallowly buried and filter feed with feathery antenna.*

Blood Worms: *Hemoglobin causes red color. They aerate beach sand as they eat their way through the layers, processing organic material as they go (like Earth worms).*

Terrestrial Insects: *Lots of beetles and flies take advantage of all the decomposition. Then lots of birds take advantage of them.*

Plastic in the OCEAN

Plastic may be one of the biggest threats to ocean health. We know relatively little about the effects other than there are enormous quantities of macro (large) plastics floating about in Texas-sized rafts, known as gyres, in five locations around the world. Beach plastics are eaten by many animals, especially young birds and mammals, who then die from impaction or poisoning, or get tangled in plastics in the water and drown. The large plastics can also break down into tiny pieces only visible by microscope—these are known as micro-plastics. Water samples are being taken all over the world to determine the extent of micro-plastic pollution. These tiny particles are likely to have devastating impacts on sea life, especially by releasing toxins into young creatures or very vulnerable species like coral and phytoplankton.

Your Plastic Use

What plastic do you actually use? Not just when traveling or adventuring, but in your daily life? The primary ingredients in plastics are petroleum products, and while recycling is certainly much better than a landfill, the recycling process is relatively wasteful and inefficient.

Things to look for:

☐ The obvious: bottled water, soda, milk, shopping bags, trash bags, food bags.

☐ Restaurant and cooking: straws, jelly containers, sometimes silverware, plastic wrap, containers for berries and salad greens, plastic-wrapped meat, egg containers.

☐ The sneaky: candy bar wrappers, micro-beads in facial scrubs or toothpaste, fleece clothing that sheds plastic micro-fibers, jewelry, non-refillable pens, non-stick cookware coating coming off when scrubbed, thermal receipt paper (e.g. gas station receipts), toilet paper comes in plastic, paper milk cartons and ice cream containers (lined with polyethylene), some tin cans are lined with plastic as are many glass jar lids, individually wrapped tea bags, and more.

How could you easily reduce your plastic use?

Ocean Birds

Murrelet

Marbled murrelets are squat, sea-going birds that spend all of their time on the ocean except for nesting. They then head inland to nest high in very large trees.

Because they nest in trees, murrelets are very vulnerable to logging, and some populations may be in danger.

Arctic waters are incredibly productive for zooplankton and fish because of the cold, mineral rich waters. This leads creatures like the Arctic tern to do some amazing migrations, documented by a tiny GPS. Scientists have clocked this 3.5 ounce bird traveling 43,000 miles every year between summer breeding grounds in the Arctic, to winter feeding grounds in the Antarctic. Alaska is one of the locations where they choose to raise their young.

Tern

Scoter

Sea-going ducks, like these Surf scoters, spend most of their time cruising out along the waves and feeding beneath the water. Alaska has several types of scoters (Black or Common and White-winged scoter). All species have goofy-looking noses on sleek, compact, black bodies.

Cormorant

Red-faced cormorants are one of four species of cormorants around Alaska. Pelagic, Brandt's, and Double-crested are the others. Red-faced are unique to Alaska and have been reported to be spreading across the state.

Cormorants have to dry their feathers. This is a classic posture.

Puffins are sea-going birds with unmistakable beaks. They were called "Sea Parrots" by early explorers. There are two species in AK: Tufted (with long, white head feathers) and Horned. Puffins, like some other sea birds, actually nest underground (3-4 feet) unless they are in particularly rocky areas where they nest in scrapes. They lay a SINGLE egg (unusual in the bird world where egg and young success is incredibly low). Their wings are made for swimming, not flying, making them awkward in the air. Because they are largely aquatic and also molt most of their feathers at once, they are very susceptible to oil spills.

Puffin

Grebe

Many birds are seasonal visitors to Alaska, coming to the productive arctic waters and near continual sunshine and plant growth to feed and raise their young. However, the winters are too bitter and barren for most of them to survive, so after a brief stay, they begin their journey back to milder climates, hundreds, thousands, or tens of thousands of miles away. Red-necked grebes often winter along the coast of California.

35

Ice and Dead Birds

Ten of thousands of dead murres and other marine seabirds have washed up on Alaskan shores in recent years. Researchers concluded that these birds starved to death. This starvation began at the bottom of the food web with phytoplankton that rely on glacial and sea ice to grow.

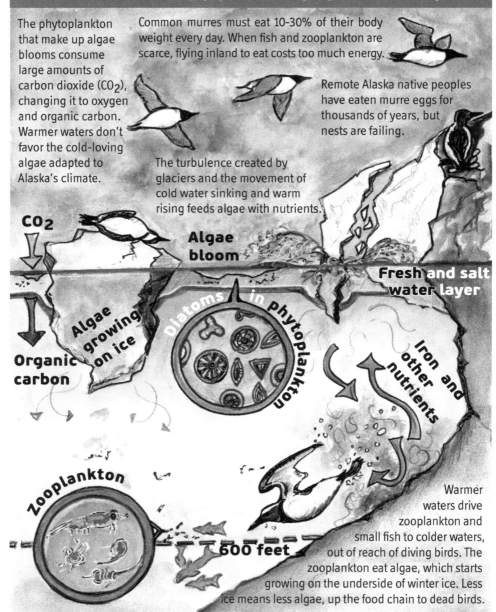

The phytoplankton that make up algae blooms consume large amounts of carbon dioxide (CO_2), changing it to oxygen and organic carbon. Warmer waters don't favor the cold-loving algae adapted to Alaska's climate.

Common murres must eat 10-30% of their body weight every day. When fish and zooplankton are scarce, flying inland to eat costs too much energy.

Remote Alaska native peoples have eaten murre eggs for thousands of years, but nests are failing.

The turbulence created by glaciers and the movement of cold water sinking and warm rising feeds algae with nutrients.

CO_2

Algae bloom

Fresh and salt water layer

Algae growing on ice

Diatoms in phytoplankton

Organic carbon

Iron and other nutrients

Zooplankton

600 feet

Warmer waters drive zooplankton and small fish to colder waters, out of reach of diving birds. The zooplankton eat algae, which starts growing on the underside of winter ice. Less ice means less algae, up the food chain to dead birds.

Lingcod are the wolverines of the ocean, with voracious appetites including eating other lingcod of the same size. Male lingcod guard the nests, so if you catch a male during spawning season it generally results in the loss of the nest (not the case with many other fish).

Black rockfish are also known as Rock bass because of their bass-shaped body with a large mouth and spiny dorsal fin. The spines are venomous and cause pain and infection. They live around 50 years! Pacific halibut eat the rockfish. They perform vertical migrations with sunset and sunrise.

Black Rockfish

Lingcod

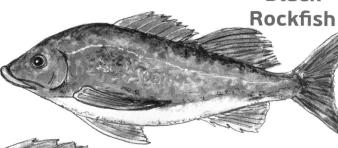

Ocean Fish you might catch

Halibut

Halibut are almost all right-eyed (both eyes on upper side.) If you catch a lefty, you just got a 1 in 20,000 chance fish. They are flat so as to hide on the ocean floor. They can be confused with Arrowtooth flounder, who have very coarse scales and prominent needle teeth. Half the females aren't sexually mature until after age 12. They can grow to 8 feet and over 500 pounds, living for 55 years!

Salmon Life Cycle

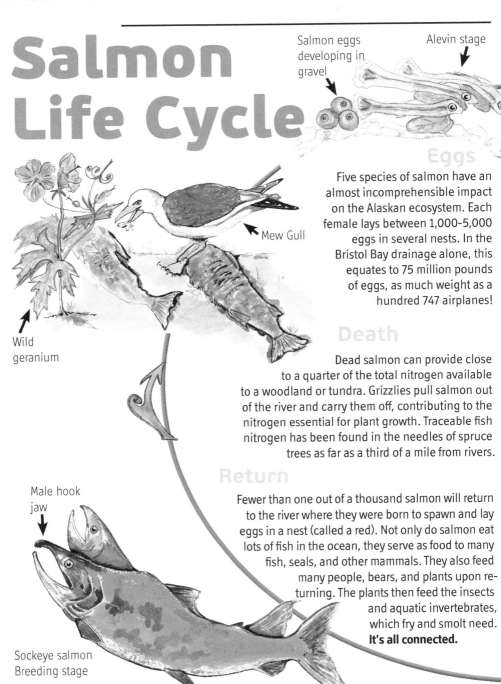

Salmon eggs developing in gravel

Alevin stage

Eggs

Five species of salmon have an almost incomprehensible impact on the Alaskan ecosystem. Each female lays between 1,000-5,000 eggs in several nests. In the Bristol Bay drainage alone, this equates to 75 million pounds of eggs, as much weight as a hundred 747 airplanes!

Mew Gull

Wild geranium

Death

Dead salmon can provide close to a quarter of the total nitrogen available to a woodland or tundra. Grizzlies pull salmon out of the river and carry them off, contributing to the nitrogen essential for plant growth. Traceable fish nitrogen has been found in the needles of spruce trees as far as a third of a mile from rivers.

Return

Fewer than one out of a thousand salmon will return to the river where they were born to spawn and lay eggs in a nest (called a red). Not only do salmon eat lots of fish in the ocean, they serve as food to many fish, seals, and other mammals. They also feed many people, bears, and plants upon returning. The plants then feed the insects and aquatic invertebrates, which fry and smolt need. **It's all connected.**

Male hook jaw

Sockeye salmon Breeding stage

Female lays eggs in gravel. Male releases sperm (milt) upstream to fertilize eggs, then female buries them.

Fish

Smolt stage

Fry stage

White tipped fins

"Char-don", Arctic char or Dolly Varden (very hard to tell apart)

Huge fin.

Arctic grayling

Prey

A tremendous number and variety of fish, like the Arctic grayling and "Char-don", eat salmon in all growth stages: eggs, alevin, fry and smolt. However if there are too many predators eating young salmon, there are fewer salmon returning to spawn, thus less food for the predatory fish. The result is a die-off, or decreased population. This relationship usually keeps a balance between predators and prey.

Obstacles

Alaska has 167 dams, some of which are on salmon spawning rivers. They greatly inhibit the ability of salmon to return from the ocean and to spawn in traditional areas. This human-made change deprives bears, birds and scavengers of the salmon meat, and the vegetation of nitrogen, making plants less nutritious for everyone from bugs to grazers, and all the way up the food chain to top predators.

Smolt out to Ocean

1-4 years later adults back from the ocean

Parasitic Sea lice

Fish

Species of Salmon

These are five species of salmon (plus one trout) in spawning colors. There is significant color variation in fish from an ocean-phase silver to the final spectacular spawning phase. The best way to tell males from females is head shape, not color.

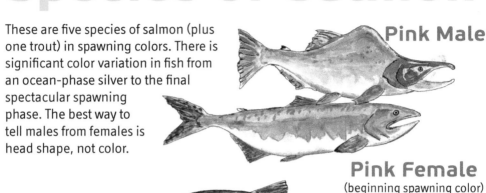

Pink Male

Pink Female
(beginning spawning color)

Coho Male

Females of Coho and Chum salmon look a lot like the males but without the hooked upper jaw.

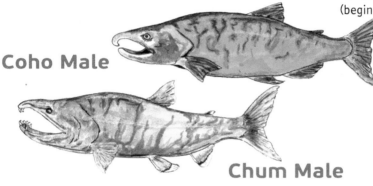

Chum Male

Sockeye Female

Sockeye salmon are thought by many to be the tastiest fish, but tough to catch by sport fisherman because they seldom bite a hook.

Sockeye Male

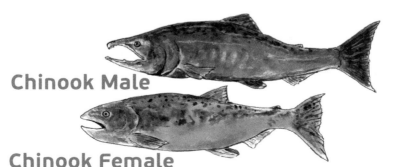

Chinook are the largest of the Pacific salmon.

Chinook Male

Chinook Female

A Trout Species

Steelhead have a green back with red stripe like a Rainbow trout, to which they are genetically identical, but differ by spending part of their life cycle in the ocean.

Steelhead Trout Male

Steelhead Female

Ocean Phase Salmon

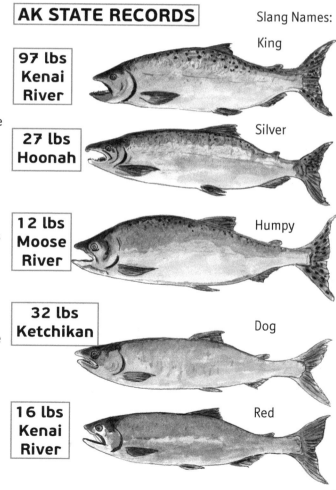

AK STATE RECORDS

Slang Names:

Chinook
Dark mouth, black gum-line
Large, sharp teeth
Tail spotted on both lobes
Large back spots

97 lbs Kenai River

King

Coho
Light mouth, white gum-line
Tail spotted only on upper lobe
Medium, sharp teeth
Spotted back
Light body toward tail

27 lbs Hoonah

Silver

Pink
White mouth, black gum-line
Almost no teeth
Large oval spots on both lobes
Pointed lower jaw
No silver on tail
Very small scales

12 lbs Moose River

Humpy

Chum
White mouth, white gum-line
Vertical bars sometimes visible
White tip on last lower fin
Body narrows toward tail
Well developed teeth
No spots

32 lbs Ketchikan

Dog

Sockeye
White mouth, white gum-line
Almost toothless
No spots
Big, bright gold eyes

16 lbs Kenai River

Red

41

Tide pool Ecosystem

Mussels: are filter feeders of the ocean, great for pulling in both food and pollutants. Their distribution is controlled by starfish.

Acorn barnacles: dentists have been trying to reconstruct the amazing glue barnacles use to attach to rocks.

Anemones: full of stinging cells for killing small fish/invertebrates. They close for protection. Green color comes from algae in tissues.

Gumboot: enormous, leathery, sea slug-like creatures. Butterfly-shaped exoskeleton. Eats seaweed and algae. Sculpins nibble at their flesh.

Chiton: light sensitive cells just below the surface allows them to sense movement above. They have eyes made of calcite (rock).

Crabs: some crabs can change their osmotic regulation allowing them to survive in different gradations of salt water (brackish to sea water.)

Nudibranch: all nudibranchs are "hermaphroditic" meaning they function reproductively as males and females at the same time.

Sea lettuce: very edible, good source of vitamin C, iron, iodine, and protein. Only two cells thick.

Hermit crab: find discarded shells to live in. They often get together for a "house party" in which they exchange shells.

Sculpin: these amazingly camouflaged fish are all over. Stop moving and watch the shallows for a while to find them even in barren-looking gravel.

Starfish: can re-grow limbs. They can also send their stomach outside their body into gaps of less than 1mm wide and 5 inches in depth.

Sea sponges: largely unchanged for 500 million years.

Sea palms: very hearty and well attached for life in heavy surf and can displace mussels. They have been over-harvested in many areas and are uncommon in AK.

Sea urchins: burrow into rocks and eat lots of kelp. However sea otters eat them, restoring balance. Each spine is attached with a ball and socket joint.

Sea cucumber: when threatened they can spit out some of their organs to distract predators. They grow the organ(s) back in about six weeks.

Ribbon kelp: kelps grow continually and contribute a large amount of organic matter to the marine ecosystem.

Limpets: can seal their shells so tightly it retains seawater, allowing them to use their gills even in air.

Barnacles: have "cirri" feeding appendages that can sweep out to find food up to two inches away.

Rockweed: gas bubbles in tip keep plant near the surface for sunlight. Like almost all seaweeds, edible (may or may not be tasty and should be rinsed).

Kelp forests: usually in deeper water than the inter-tidal zone, however they can drift in and attach to rocks in the shallows. Major habitat for many species.

Sea snails: some can secrete an anesthetic from their proboscis to immobilize prey.

Sea otters: are key for balance in the intertidal zone.

A Whale

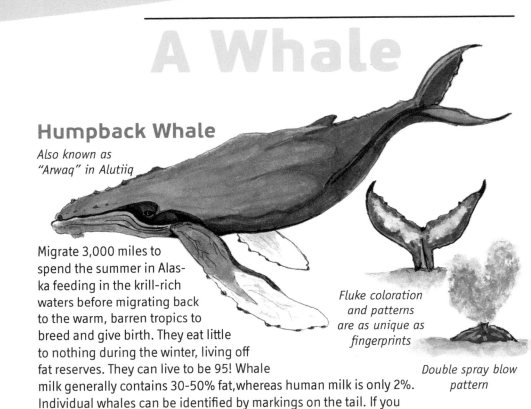

Humpback Whale

*Also known as
"Arwaq" in Alutiiq*

Migrate 3,000 miles to
spend the summer in Alaska feeding in the krill-rich
waters before migrating back
to the warm, barren tropics to
breed and give birth. They eat little
to nothing during the winter, living off
fat reserves. They can live to be 95! Whale
milk generally contains 30-50% fat, whereas human milk is only 2%.
Individual whales can be identified by markings on the tail. If you
get a photo of the tail it can be submitted to help researchers.

*Fluke coloration
and patterns
are as unique as
fingerprints*

*Double spray blow
pattern*

Harbor Porpoise

One of the smallest marine
mammals weighing about
150 lbs. They sometimes
venture up rivers and
have been seen
hundreds of miles
from sea. All too
often killed
as com-
mercial
fishing
"by-catch". Mostly soli-
tary and show little curiosity toward boats.
On the menu of orcas and sharks.

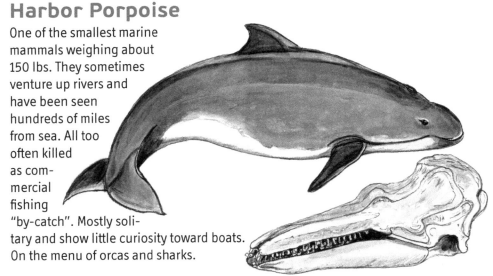

of a Tail

Orca

*Also known
as Killer
whales or
in Alutiiq as
"Arlluk".*

Single spray

Actually a member of the dolphin family. There are two populations of orcas in Alaska: residents and migrants. Resident pods seem to prefer eating fish, while the transients seem to prefer marine mammals. Orcas can be identified by white marks behind the main fin and an extremely tall, pointed fin. Pods can be identified by the sounds they make. *Arlluk* can live to be well beyond 80 years old.

Dall's Porpoise

*It's all a
matter of
scale! Dall's
porpoise
escaping
orca*

Also known as "Mangaq" in Alutiiq

Coloration and shape somewhat resemble that of the orca whale, except they are much smaller and have a much smaller dorsal fin. One of the fastest marine mammals with speeds of 34 mph, they can often be identified by the "rooster tail" splash trail they leave. Often in large pods, quite curious and social.

Sea otters use tools such as rocks and bones to open shellfish and crush crabs. They eat most meals floating on their backs. They tie themselves and their babies into the kelp to keep from floating away. They often travel in family or social groups.

Tools and Flippers

Sea Otters

These giant water weasels are a keystone predator in the complex ecosystem of kelp forests. A keystone is the central stone of an arch, without which the entire structure falls down. Keystone species are so important that entire ecosystems are drastically different without the presence of this one species. Otters eat crabs, fish, and sea urchins. The urchins graze on kelp and, if unchecked, demolish entire kelp forests upon which so many species depend. Prince William Sound has one of the largest populations of Sea otters anywhere. They were hunted for their warm fur, which is the densest of any mammal. They need this incredible coat because, unlike other marine mammals, they have no insulating blubber to help keep warm.

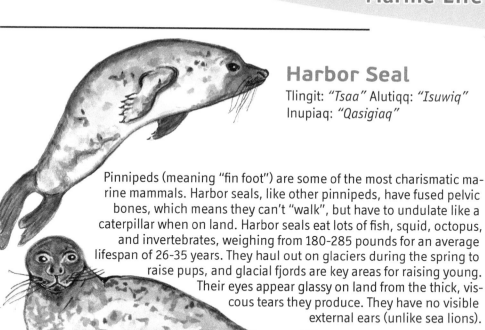

Harbor Seal

Tlingit: *"Tsaa"* Alutiqq: *"Isuwiq"*
Inupiaq: *"Qasigiaq"*

Pinnipeds (meaning "fin foot") are some of the most charismatic marine mammals. Harbor seals, like other pinnipeds, have fused pelvic bones, which means they can't "walk", but have to undulate like a caterpillar when on land. Harbor seals eat lots of fish, squid, octopus, and invertebrates, weighing from 180-285 pounds for an average lifespan of 26-35 years. They haul out on glaciers during the spring to raise pups, and glacial fjords are key areas for raising young. Their eyes appear glassy on land from the thick, viscous tears they produce. They have no visible external ears (unlike sea lions).

Steller Sea Lions

Aleut: *qawax*

Listed as endangered west of longitude 144°W. The population seems to be stabilizing, except in the Aleutian Islands. They can weigh 2,500 pounds and females can live for 30 years. They can dive to a depth of 1,500 feet. At that depth, the pressure is 650 pounds per square inch! This pressure would be like trying to hold a riding lawn mower on your thumb!

Native Cultures

The Native Alaskans were, and still are, hardy and skilled people. Each group has its own complex and rich culture. Traditionally hunting and fishing played critical roles in survival, because plants were scarce for many winter months. Drying and smoking fish and meat were important for long-term food storage and helped shape these cultures.

Athabascan:

Traditionally inhabited the interior of Alaska, often along the river corridors. There are 11 Athabascan groups identified by their language. Very skilled hunters and trappers.

Traditional home regions of native peoples.

Inupiaq and St. Lawernce Island Yupik

Athabascan

Yup'ik and Cup'ik

Aleut and Alutiiq:

The Aleut and Alutiiq traditionally inhabited the rugged Aleutian Island chain and the southern coast of Alaska. Like the Yup'ik, they often made underground shelters to protect themselves from a very cold and wet climate. Their diet was similar to many of the other peoples but also included many shellfish and crabs. Very skilled at ocean travel.

Sun Glasses

The sun off the water and the snow is SO bright! It was the same for native people, so they invented sunglasses by carving and assembling wooden sun masks with slits for the eyes. They also made these out of bone.

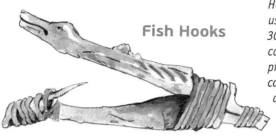

Fish Hooks

Halibut Hook: This fishing technique was used by many of the cultures in AK to catch 30-40 pound halibut. This hook is made from carved alder wood with spruce root wrappings holding the two pieces of wood and the caribou bone barb in place. The carving is a "spirit helper." Many different materials were used but the basic design was similar through many cultures.

Inupiaq and St. Lawrence Island Yupik:

The most arctic of the Alaskan people, skilled at winter travel and survival. They commonly hunted seals and whales, using blubber for food and as heating and cooking fuel. Skilled at crafts and functional arts such as decorative clothing. A traditional winter dwelling was the Igloo.

Yup'ik and Cup'ik:

Traditionally inhabited western Alaska and the Russian far east. Like many of the interior people, the Yup'ik and Cap'ik were semi-nomadic hunter-gatherers. They utilized a wide range of foods including: salmon and other fish, seals, land mammals, birds, berries and roots. They traveled with both sled dogs and kayaks.

Eyak
Tlingit
Haida
Tsimshian:

These four cultures inhabited the islands and coast of southeast Alaska and Canada, but were very different. Many of these people maintained permanent villages and were/are skilled woodworkers, building canoes that could hold 60 paddlers, as well as elaborate pieces of art (totem poles). Tlingit means "People of the Tides."

Rain Jackets

The First Gore-Tex! This light, waterproof rain jacket was made of intestines (many different types of animal from Brown bear to seal), sewn together with sinew (tendons pounded, fibers pulled apart and then rolled back together to form string). The intestines are nearly see-through, and the edges were lined with fur.

The Tundra is
WARMING

Excess carbon dioxide and methane in the atmosphere increases the rate of global warming. The warming planet is melting the frozen layers of soil, permafrost, for the first time in thousands of years. The organic compounds trapped   by the soil begin to decompose and form more atmospheric compounds.

Warmer temperatures also contribute to tundra fires, which release incredible amounts of carbon dioxide. However, warmer temperatures and more unfrozen soil leads to increased plant growth, which uptakes CO_2.

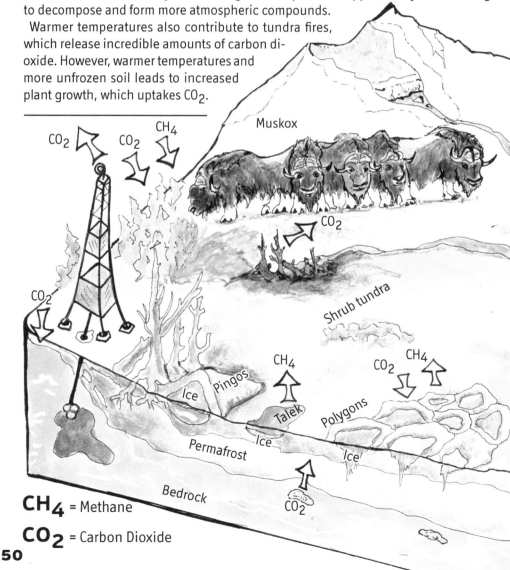

CH_4 = Methane

CO_2 = Carbon Dioxide

Animals like the muskox, a relic of the last ice age, have such dense fur they can't afford for winters to get any shorter or summers hotter. The Arctic fox also has very dense and camouflaged white fur for winter. As winters become shorter, the Red fox is able to push deeper into Arctic fox territory and compete for chicks and eggs from the huge populations of ground-nesting birds such as Tundra swans.

The balance of prey to predators is crucial to the success of many species who come to the tundra to breed. Lemmings provide food for many predators in the area, but they are boom and bust populations influenced by the availability of tundra plant species.

Kittiwakes rely on small fish for their massive nesting colonies. However, as the tundra warms it drains more sediments and organic matter into the ocean, causing algae blooms and acidifying the water.

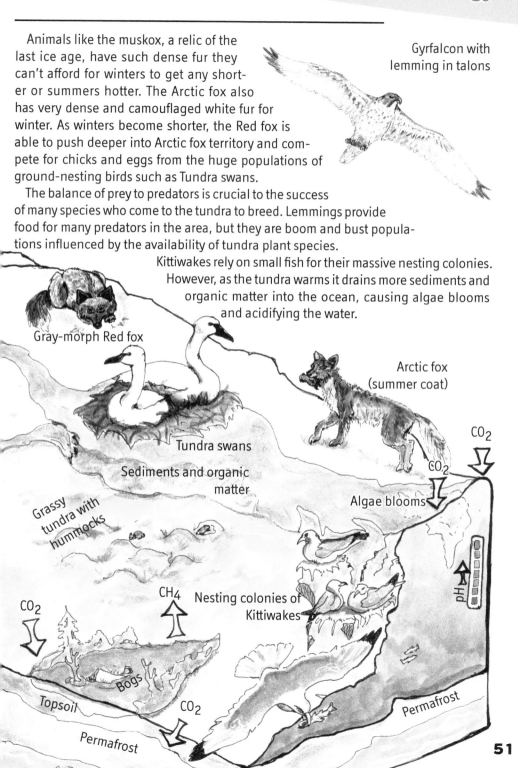

Gyrfalcon with lemming in talons

Gray-morph Red fox

Arctic fox (summer coat)

Tundra swans

Sediments and organic matter

Algae blooms

CO_2

CO_2

Grassy tundra with hummocks

CO_2

CH_4

Nesting colonies of Kittiwakes

pH

Topsoil

Bogs

CO_2

Permafrost

Permafrost

The ROCK Cycle

Rocks seem like they last forever, but really they are constantly changing from one form to another. Each type of rock may change in a few million years. The rock cycle has an enormous impact on everything in an ecosystem from weather patterns to the particular type of vegetation. Alaska is also one of the most dynamic places geologically, with over 50 active volcanoes (since 1760), and an average of 1,500 - 3,000 earthquakes a month! This is 11% of the world's earthquakes and 52% of the earthquakes in the U.S. Much of the rock cycle and active Alaskan geology is driven by the Pacific Plate sliding under the Continental Plate (subduction), creating tremendous heat and pressure, melting rocks and forcing them back to the surface.

Metamorphic

Any pre-existing rock type can be transformed into another at the molecular level when exposed to extreme heat and pressure, either by being buried deep beneath the earth's surface, or by tectonic processes such as colliding plates. Metamorphic rock is most easily identified when you can see folds and bends in the mineral layers. These rocks are brought to the surface via uplift.

Igneous

Rock that is formed from cooled magma. When magma cools slowly, deep in the earth, it is called "Intrusive". Ex: granite, diorite, and gabbro. These often have large visible crystal grains. "Extrusive" is when this happens on the surface. The cooling is relatively fast and the individual crystal grains are usually very small. Ex: basalt, rhyolite, pumice, and tuff. Many of the AK ranges are largely made of igneous rocks. The Wranglles and Denali are mostly granite.

Sedimentary

Minerals are deposited in the oceans or on land from erosion, weathering, and marine invertebrates. These become cemented by pressure or chemicals into "sedimentary" rocks. Ex: limestone, sandstone, shale, and the ubiquitous greywacke, which makes up many of the marine cliffs.

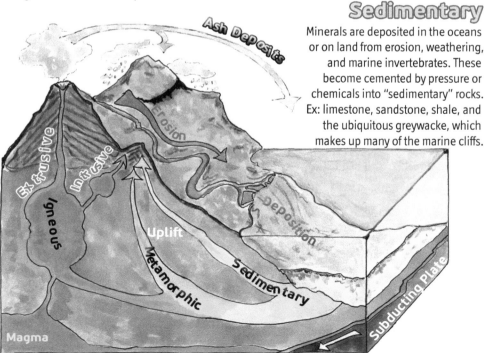

And Resources

Gold

Since the 1800's, gold mining has been an important driving force for the economy. Gold is often associated with quartz, which itself can be found within intrusive granite, or where super-heated quartz cooled in rock seams near shale. Alaska gold mining is still a controversial issue today, and abandoned equipment and tailings piles (unwanted rock) can be found even in remote areas of the state. Gold mining in Canada is polluting streams and leading to new dams for hydroelectric power to run the mines, which is affecting downstream Alaskan waters and salmon.

> **Fort Knox Gold Mine, Fairbanks, AK processes 29.8 tons of rock for every ounce of gold!**

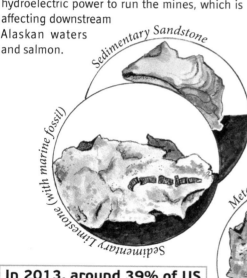

Igneous Granite

Sedimentary Sandstone

Sedimentary Limestone (with marine fossil)

Igneous Gold vein in Quartz

Metamorphic Layered Rock

Metamorphic Coal Seam

> **In 2013, around 39% of US energy came from coal and only 6% from renewable sources. The remaining 55% is from natural gas, nuclear, and hydroelectric.**

Coal

Alaska has about half of all US coal, however, much of it is inaccessible without major infrastructure development. Coal is a metamorphic rock formed by large amounts of carbon, mostly from ancient swamps and vegetation, buried by sediment then heated and compressed over 250 million years. You may see coal or coal mining in surprisingly remote and pristine areas of Alaska, and dark black coal seams are visible in river banks, road cuts, and on exposed hillsides.

R GLACIAL
E
T
R
E
A
T

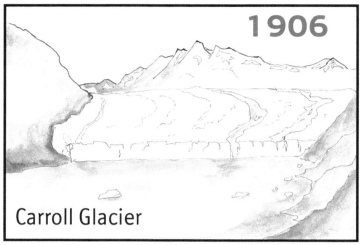

1906

Carroll Glacier

Global warming has led to significant glacial melting, as seen is these watercolored versions of reference photos of the Carroll Glacier.

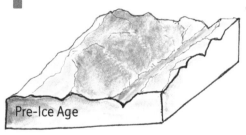

Pre-Ice Age

Before the ice: most of the mountains were gentle and rounded, being only sculpted by wind and water. Rivers carve v-shaped valleys, which are relatively narrow.

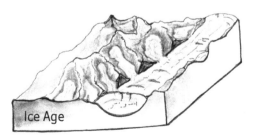

Ice Age

During the ice age: glaciers formed where snow fell but never completely melted. The sharp, grinding ice starts tearing away at soil and bedrock, sculpting the landscape.

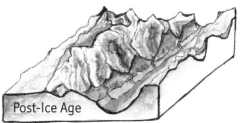

Post-Ice Age

After the ice: the sharp, dramatic landscaped is revealed, with wide, u-shaped valleys and steep, dramatic cliff-faces. High alpine lakes are left in deep pits, and hanging valleys above the main glacier's path.

Carroll Glacier retreated approx. 1 mile. Muir Glacier shrunk 31 miles!

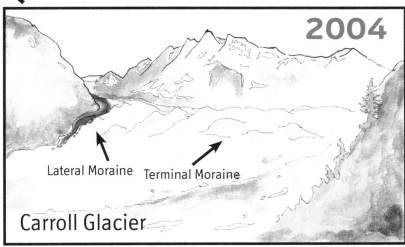

2004

Lateral Moraine   **Terminal Moraine**

Carroll Glacier

Moraines are the ground rock and debris pushed down by the glacier. Notice the greening of landscapes surrounding melted glaciers.

Glaciers are formed by snowfall that doesn't melt. Eventually the many years of snow will become heavy enough to pressure the crystals into denser and denser ice. The denser the ice, the more red light it absorbs, reflecting back only blue light, giving old, dense glaciers that beautiful blue cast.

Glacial ice can be thousands of feet thick, hauling incalculable amounts of rock and soil along with it as it moves downhill with gravity, sometimes merely inches per day, sometimes fifty feet. The soil and rocks deposited by a glacier after it melts away are called moraines. They can be seen all over as the result of continental glaciers. In Alaska, you can see these land-forming process as they happen! You can also spot the boulder remnants, ponds and scars they've left behind. But hurry! Global warming may give you a limited window to see this magic.

When glaciers grind their way over large rocks they gouge lines, or striations, into the polished surface. You (and the Alaska marmot) can look to see which way the glacier was traveling.

Osprey are diving raptors. They spot fish from the air then plunge into the water. After tremendous effort to get back up, they straighten their legs into line to fly the fish in a face-forward, aerodynamic position.

Short-tailed weasel, or "ermine" are both ferocious and also trapped for fur.

Muskrats sometimes live with beavers in their lodges. Several million are trapped per year, the most valuable U.S. fur species.

Common loons have legs placed far back on the body, lousy for walking but great water propellers for catching fish and crayfish. Beavers create great habitat for fishing birds.

Moose eat a lot of aquatic plants and even swim underwater to get tasties. Riparian habitats are essential for moose survival, making beaver good habitat partners.

Beavers completely change the habitat around them. Their dams drown trees, and eventually, when the damn fills in, the rich pond soil forms lush meadows. Look for beaver-chewed trees (they take them down with their chiseled front teeth). Beaver will slide logs great distances, leaving long drag marks.

Beaver have webbed hind feet for efficient swimming, but fingers on the front for dexterity.

Bears consider beaver a fatty, tasty meal, which means beavers in bear-dense areas (like AK) have particularly dense lodges to discourage bears from pulling them apart, as well as bigger dams and deeper ponds.

Beaver need several feet of unfrozen water below the winter ice, as well as an air-pocket to breath.

B U S Y as a B E A V E R

Beaver dams are interwoven sticks to "dam" water into ponds, providing essential aquatic habitat and protection.

Beaver's thick, dense paddle tails are used as rudders when swimming, and good for communication when slapped loudly against the water.

Beavers don't hibernate, so they need an underwater pantry (a larder) for tree cambium to eat all winter. They have special gut bacteria that digest the high-fiber diet.

Beaver pelts make great felt for hats, which where considered stylish in Europe. From 1853-1877 The Hudson Bay Company recorded 3 million beaver pelts from AK!

All about Trees

Pika

Black and White Spruce

Slide Alder

Cottonwood

Willow

Red Alder

Shrubby Cinquefoil

Ferns

Dipper

Golden-crowned Sparrow

Beluga Whale

Copperbush

(and some amazing creatures)

Snowy Owl

Paper Birch

Aspen

Sitka Spruce

Cedar

Hemlock

Porcupine

American Pine Marten

Three-toed Woodpecker

Walrus

Alaskan Hare

Gray Wolf

Critters

Tree-dependent species like the **American Pine marten** (weasel family) rely on a healthy, mixed forest with lots of squirrels to eat. They have long, sharp claws for easy tree climbing into squirrel nests (dreys). They also raid bird nests, so can be great for bird language.

The **Snowy owl** is most likely seen in the open, nesting on the tundra. So treeline, where it's too cold and harsh for tree growth, is essential for their survival. Global warming is moving treeline further north, shrinking treeless habitat.

The **Gray wolf** is adaptable, good at slinking through trees, or hunting in packs out on the open tundra.

Arctic hares rely on willows, alders, and other shrubs for both food and shelter.

Pika need a lack of trees. They live in boulder fields on the edge of meadows. They hay plants (dry them) to survive the long winter.

Porcupines eat trees! They use long chisel teeth to chew into the cambium, leaving big patch scars. They have special bacteria to digest wood.

Golden-crowned sparrows are often spotted in Slide alder by their yellow head feathers.

Three-toed woodpeckers do have only three toes (only one other woodpecker can claim this missing digit)

Dippers walk underwater to feed! They perch on rocks, bobbing constantly. Their nests are amazing domes made out of moss.

Did you see the **River otter** tracks as they ➜ belly-slid past the nest?

Walruses, like Polar bears, are very affected by global warming. They need to stay around shallow waters to feed on clams and other aquatic life, but they also need significant-sized ice chunks to haul out on to relax, warm up, and keep their young from drowning. This ice is becoming scarcer. Trees uptake huge amounts of carbon.

Beluga whales "molt" every year, and head into shallow waters to rub up along gravel bars to remove old skin. They are white to gray, very soft looking, and incredibly talkative. Trees slow down water, forming gravel bars.

Trees of the Coast

Red Alder

Cedar

Sitka Spruce

Hemlock

Hemlock *Tsuga sp.*

Hemlock have a wind-swept, clumpy look, appearing one-sided along shorelines or windy ridges. They have soft, flat, short needles and small, dark brown cones that, like the spruce, are very thin and insubstantial compared to the cones of pine trees. Hemlock are a very important source of alpha cellulose for making: cellophane, rayon, yarn and plastic. Peoples of SE. Alaska used to make a coarse bread from the inner bark.

Cedar *Callitropsis or Thuja sp.*

Cedar, like the coastal Yellow cedar, have scaly branches instead of hanging needles, and odd-looking, round, pointy cones. The bark is generally stringy. The wood was (and still is) highly valued for straight grain and resistance to insects, but the trees are dying in large numbers. This is thought to be the result of root freezing, because global warming has reduced snow layers which normally insulated the roots.

Sitka Spruce *Picea sitchensis*

Spruce trees, like the Sitka spruce, have very dense, very spiny needles. Their cones are light tan and papery. Spruces are very susceptible to heart rot, so they can fall even when green because the middle of the tree has been weakened by fungus. Spruce needle tea (the fresh tips) is a great source of Vitamin C and one of our favorites. Moose also approve, eating the tips in winter.

Red Alder *Alnus rubra*

Red alder looks similar to Slide alder except Red alder is almost always a tree. The bark is generally gray with long lenticulars (stretched oval marks). These deciduous trees have thin bark which makes them good browse in winter for moose, and all year for porcupines who eat the cambium in large patches. Red alder is one of the few plant species to fix soil nitrogen into a usable form. This makes Red alder a key species for improving soil quality for all other plants.

Inland Trees

Young female cones
(unfertilized)
Male cones (pollen)➔

Catkin

Black Spruce	White Spruce	Birch	Aspen	Cottonwood
☐ Classic shrubby top look ☐ Twigs have fuzzy brown hairs (bend back needles to expose) ☐ Spiny spruce needles	☐ Classic, even round look ☐ Twigs DO NOT have fuzzy brown hairs. ☐ Spiny spruce needles	☐ Mature bark white and peeling ☐ Immature bark has reddish hues. ☐ Oval shaped leaves with course double-tooth	☐ White bark with lots of black scars. ☐ Young or wet bark is green from chlorophyll in bark. ☐ Leaf stem is perpendicular to leaf plane, allowing leaf to "quake" in the wind. Turn orange in fall.	☐ Thick, corky gray bark at base ☐ Upper bark brown to white to red-gray. ☐ Generally confined to edge of water courses. ☐ Usually large leaves.

Black Spruce   *Picea mariana*

A tree highly specialized for slow growth in the arctic; a tree 1 inch in diameter was recorded at 160 years old. Because of the impermeable permafrost, this tree can survive with roots that are only 8-12 inches deep. Branches touching soil can grow roots, eventually becoming another tree. The needles make a nice tea; roots were used to hold birch-bark canoes together.

White Spruce   *Picea glauca*

This common tree throughout the boreal forest typically has a conical shape. Native peoples used the light, strong wood for making snowshoes and other tools. The sap was used for gluing arrowheads to shafts and the bark was used for making bowls, cooking pots and baskets. Spruce tip tea is high in Vitamin C.

Paper Birch   *Betula papyrifera*

Often a pioneer species after fire or human disturbance. Note how many Paper birch are visible around the greater Anchorage area. A very important tree to native people throughout its range. The sap is sweet and can be boiled to make a syrup. The bark will help you light a fire even in wet conditions and was used in everything from baskets to canoes to shelters.

Aspen   *Populus tremuloides*

Aspen groves are a "clone," growing from a single, long-lived root system. One clone in Utah is estimated to be 80,000 years old! The fire strategy for aspens is to allow the trunks to burn and then regenerate quickly from the large root system. This process is faster than their main competitor, conifer trees. Because of climate change Alaska is experiencing more fires, which may favor aspen.

Balsam Poplar/Cottonwood   *Populus sp.*

Closely related to the more southerly cottonwood and sharing many similar properties. Dead branches and roots make excellent bow-drill fire sets. The winter/spring leaf-buds have a sticky sap that can be used as a topical pain reliever in salves. Steam from leaf-bud tea or buds mixed with honey has been used to treat coughs.

Cold Adaptations

Trees have to be tricky not to burst by freezing in extra cold winters. Hormone changes in the fall allow the tree to "harden off" or prepare for cold by shedding excess water while developing thicker, more resilient cell walls. Finally, the carbohydrates and sugars in the cell chemically allow the water in the cell to freeze without expanding or developing sharp crystals, "vitrifacation".

Shrubs

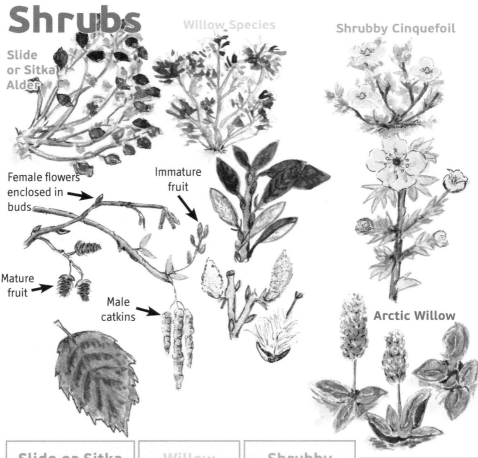

Willow Species

Shrubby Cinquefoil

Slide or Sitka Alder

Female flowers enclosed in buds

Immature fruit

Mature fruit

Male catkins

Arctic Willow

Slide or Sitka Alder	Willow Species	Shrubby Cinquefoil	Arctic Willow
☐ Grows in avalanche chutes. Incredibly dense. ☐ Shrub = lots of stems rather than one single trunk. ☐ Lots of tooth to the leaf (very pointy). ☐ Mature fruit like mini-pine cones. Only found on alder. ☐ If you bushwhack through these, you won't forget them.	☐ Several species in Alaska. ☐ Shiny green on top of leaf, fuzzy white hairs beneath. ☐ Fuzzy white seedheads. ☐ Upright catkins. ☐ Leaves rarely have any tooth, and usually long and narrow.	☐ Yellow flowers. ☐ Small, pointy leaves with many lobes (like fingers). ☐ Can be a sizeable shrub to single, woody stem. ☐ Highly domesticated and adaptable species. You might see this plant in gardens, or wild across the U.S.	☐ Itty-bitty shrubs made to survive arctic weather. ☐ Upright catkins are largest part of shrub. Very distinctive. ☐ Waxy, round leaves. ☐ Can sometimes see woody branches creeping along ground. ☐ Can find several species of dwarf willow in Alaska.

Slide Alder   *Alnus viridis Athabasca: Kxiiib*

Also know as Sitka or Green alder. Can be 5-30 feet tall. It often colonizes avalanche slopes and behind glacial recessions. It has nitrogen-fixing nodes on its roots and can fix 55 pounds of nitrogen per acre. Alder was used for making bows, snowshoe frames and spoons. The bark was used for a red dye and the wood was a favorite for smoking fish. The twigs and leaves are eaten by rabbits, muskrat and many other small rodents. Look for chewing scars.

Willow Species   *Salix sp. Tlingit: ch'áal'*

There are over 40 willow species in Alaska (common: Alaska, Bebb, Black, and Little Tree willow). Willows are a very important food for many critters, from mice to moose. Willows are very useful for making baskets, fish traps, and tent frames. The bark contains salicylic acid, the active ingredient in aspirin. Chewing stems or bark tea has been used for treating pain for over 6,000 years.

Shrubby Cinquefoil   *Pentaphylloides fruticosa*

A small to medium shrub rarely more then 4 feet tall, cinquefoil is not an important browse for ungulates, but is eaten in moderation possibly to gain nutrients not found in other plants. The papery bark makes a great tinder for starting fires. Many native tribes drank a tea of the leaves, reported to be high in calcium.

Arctic Willow   *Salix arctica*

Look closely or you might miss this small shrub. Highly adapted for cold and wind, it may be only a few inches tall. It has no taproots, only lateral roots adapted for frozen ground. Many tundra animals eat the willow including caribou, lemmings and ptarmigan (largely dependent on the buds). Natives ate the inner parts of young shoots and roots. Leaves are very high in Vitamin C. The wood parts were used as fuel, and fibrous seed heads were used as wicks in seal oil lanterns called a "Kudlik."

Sword fern: Look on the underside of the fronds for reproductive bodies (spores) in structures called sporangia. Sword ferns were traditionally used to line steam cooking pits and as flooring or bedding.

Fire from Sticks!

(With the helpful assistance of a knife and a short piece of cord)

Bowdrill Basics

Not all trees or woods are equal. This is an excellent reason to work on your tree and shrub identification. The easiest are: cottonwood, cedar, aspen, willow, and tamarack/larch. Alder and birch are tougher, whereas the pine, fir and spruce trees are extremely difficult to use (almost impossible, but not quite).

How to start: Select some DEAD, DRY, but not rotten, wood. Here are some rough dimensions to use:

Handhold: Just needs to fit in your hand and keep the spindle from popping out. This wood can be anything, and is sometimes helped by being a harder wood.

Spindle: Ideally ¾ of an inch to an inch after being whittled down, or a very straight branch you don't have to carve. You can get away with bigger or smaller, but it takes more skill.

Fireboard: Roughly 2" wide. This is an ideal minimum. You can use a larger fireboard easily.

Bow: 2-3 foot long stick that is ½"-1" in diameter. A slightly curved branch can make things a touch easier, but straight will do. Tie your cordage of choice (shoelace, leather thong, sinew or strong, thin string) firmly to one end. You will need to adjust the tension on the other end, so an easily adjustable knot is handy.

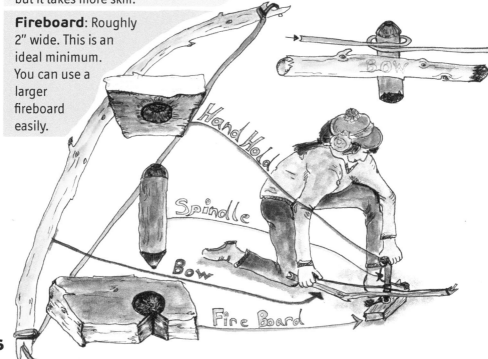

Order of operations:

You need to **make a shallow depression** with a knife or sharp rock for your spindle to sit in both your fireboard and handhold. Measure in from the edge of your fireboard a little more than half the diameter of your spindle. This should be the deepest point in the socket. Your handhold depression should be in the center.

Sharpen your spindle on both ends. You will need to keep shaping the fireboard end throughout the process.

Put your foot, often best barefoot, on top of your fireboard to hold it stable.

Twist your spindle in the bow-string. It should feel like it wants to pop out of your hand.

Tuck your handhold arm around your knee, with your handhold pressing firmly down on the spindle and your forearm steadied against your shin.

Try to **bow** with steady, even strokes, rotating the spindle against the fireboard to burn in a nice, black socket. Don't be surprised if your spindle pops out. A LOT! This takes practice, the right amount of pressure from your handhold, and the right amount of tension on your bow-string. Keep adjusting until you find what works.

Once you have a good round impression in the fireboard and handhold, **cut the all important notch.** This is where black dust will collect and your ember will form! It should be a 1/8 pie-slice cut going nearly, but not quite, to the center of your socket.

Place a little tinder bundle just at the edge of your notch to catch the ember. Now **back to bowing.** Slowly. Faster. Faster. Oh my gosh that's a terrible noise and smoke is pouring out. Pop! Spindle flies across the clearing. Sigh. Start over. Better yet, get a friend to help you bow by holding the other end and pulling as you push, then visa-versa. Bow drills are tiring. When you get a tiny coal, cradle it carefully in your tinder bundle of dry, shredded bark, blow gently but insistently, and finally you'll see a flame made from sticks and a small piece of rope. It is absolutely amazing!

(Background) Tamarack, or larch trees, are deciduous evergreens. Their tufts of needles turn yellow and orange in the fall before dropping off.

The POWER of PLANTS

Plants connect us to a place like few other things. At a glance, plants tell a tremendous amount about an ecosystem: where water is, where it may be safe to camp, what critters may be around. For primitive people, plants provided most of their needs, and even for us they still do! Think of cotton, wood homes, and veggies at the store. One of the best parts about learning plants is they don't run away and you don't need special equipment to study them—just your desire to learn more. We like using the pattern method developed by Thomas J. Elpel for plant families.

Beyond Name Memorization

Why touch, smell, and taste plants? Multi-sense learning builds memory connections faster than sight and sound alone, with taste being one of the strongest connections. Once tasted, you will not often forget a plant. However, if you never EAT any of these plants, still knowing edibility gives you something much more interesting to discuss than just the plant's name. We talk a lot about eating plants in this book. We are not suggesting that you should subsist off wild plants. Instead, interacting with plants builds a connection and understanding of how an ecosystem functions, as well as giving you a feeling of self-sufficiency, even if all you do is sample a few herbs. A few tastes here and there make a minimal impact on wild places, but a huge impact on your outdoor experience. LNT (Leave No Trace® techniques): Sample plants based on abundance. Take no more than 1 in 10 plants in an area and replant roots when you can.

How to Use Plants Safely

Learn the few poisonous plants first. Only eat and use plants you are **100%** sure are safe. Don't eat any plant until you are sure of at least 3 identifying features of the plant. For bluebells it might be: 1. Drooping purple/ blue flowers, 2. Elliptical, alternating leaves, 3. Leaves have distinctive smell suggestive of oysters. This will help ensure you are really looking at the plant and its traits, not just jumping to conclusions. Of all the plants in Alaska, very few are poisonous (< 2%). Around 69% of plants are non-toxic, but not really edible, and about 29% are edible, and some are delicious!

Most TOXIC — Must Know

Water Hemlock
Poison Hemlock
Monkshood
False Hellebore  Deadliest of the Deadlies
Baneberry
Wild Iris
Death Camas
Larkspur and most Buttercups
Some of the Pea Family Pods
Many Mushrooms (I.D. VERY difficult)
Cow Parsnip (possibility of severe skin reactions)

Cow Parsnip

Brassicaceae

Mustard Family

Key Features

4 Petals
6 Stamen
  - 4 Tall and
  - 2 Short

Leaves or seeds often form "raceme" (like spiral staircase)

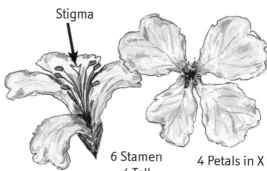

Stigma

6 Stamen
4 Tall
2 Short

4 Petals in X or H Shape

All mustard can be eaten, at least in moderation.

Not all are tasty.

Many of our common veggies are mustards: broccoli, cabbage, wasabi, watercress, brussel sprouts, radishes, etc.

Common wild mustards are: wallflower, rockcress, and draba.

If you learn the key features for this family, you just learned over 3,000 edible plants!

Parry's Wallflower

"Race Me" = Raceme structure. Like a spiral staircase up leaves or seed pods.

Mint Family

Key Features

Opposite leaves
Square stem
Aromatic

Most mints like boggy soils and wet locations. In the arctic they can be found near "pingos" (hill on tundra with core of ice)

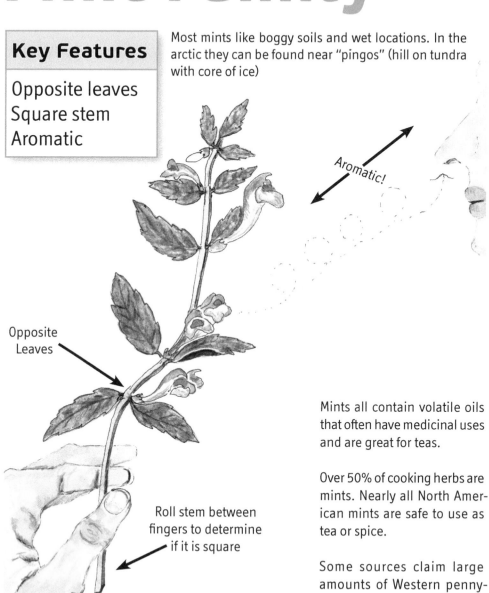

Aromatic!

Opposite Leaves

Roll stem between fingers to determine if it is square

Skullcap

Mints all contain volatile oils that often have medicinal uses and are great for teas.

Over 50% of cooking herbs are mints. Nearly all North American mints are safe to use as tea or spice.

Some sources claim large amounts of Western penny-royal (*Monardella odoratissima*) may be toxic. Large amounts = 20 cups of tea per day. That's a lot of tea!

Lilaceae

Lily Family

<table>
<tr><td colspan="2">

Key Features

Parts in 3's:
3 or 6 stamen and petals
Parallel veins
</td></tr>
</table>

Queen's Cup

Berries are toxic!

6 Petals

6 Stamen

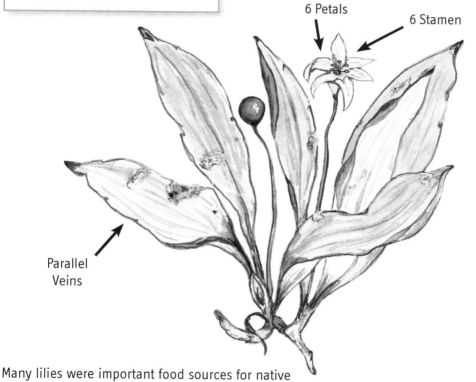

Parallel
Veins

Many lilies were important food sources for native
people. A few very toxic members of this family (False
hellebore, Death camas) have been recently moved to other plant families based on
genetic sequencing. However, they still have lily features, and may be moved back into
the Lily family once botanists have stopped debating.

Common lilies include: onions, garlics, chives, leeks, and tulips. Note: Yellow Pond lily
(Nuphar sp.) is NOT a true lily and is NOT edible.

Pea Family

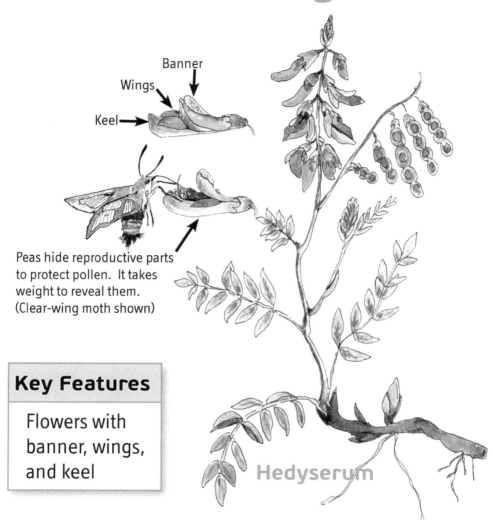

Banner

Wings

Keel

Peas hide reproductive parts to protect pollen. It takes weight to reveal them. (Clear-wing moth shown)

Hedyserum

Key Features

Flowers with banner, wings, and keel

Plants in this family include: string beans, peas, lupines, clovers, vetches, locoweeds, locusts, mesquite, and acacias trees. Nearly all the pea family plants are nitrogen fixers and aid in fertilizing soil. Don't be fooled by tasty-looking wild pea pods. Many are edible; some are **TOXIC**. A type of Hedyserum is the plant that stars in the book & movie *Into the Wild*. Toxicology results show very low levels of toxins in the seeds, indicating Hedyserum (Wild potato) is very unlikely to have killed Christopher McCandless.

Asteraceae

Aster Family

Key Features
Disk flower often surrounded by ray flowers

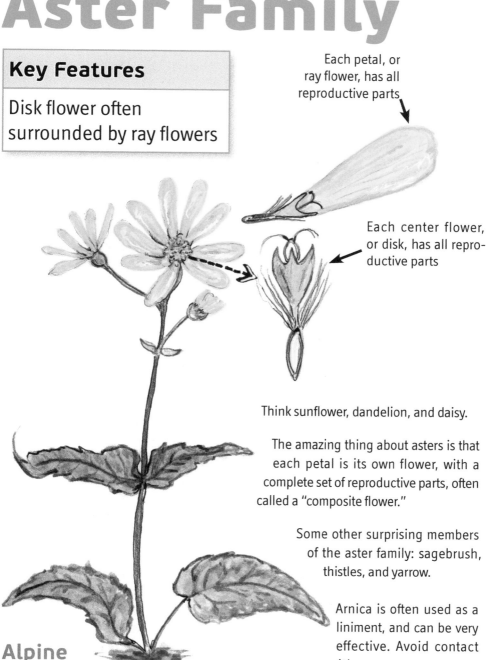

Each petal, or ray flower, has all reproductive parts

Each center flower, or disk, has all reproductive parts

Think sunflower, dandelion, and daisy.

The amazing thing about asters is that each petal is its own flower, with a complete set of reproductive parts, often called a "composite flower."

Some other surprising members of the aster family: sagebrush, thistles, and yarrow.

Arnica is often used as a liniment, and can be very effective. Avoid contact with any mucous membranes (gums, etc.)

Alpine Arnica

Parsley Family

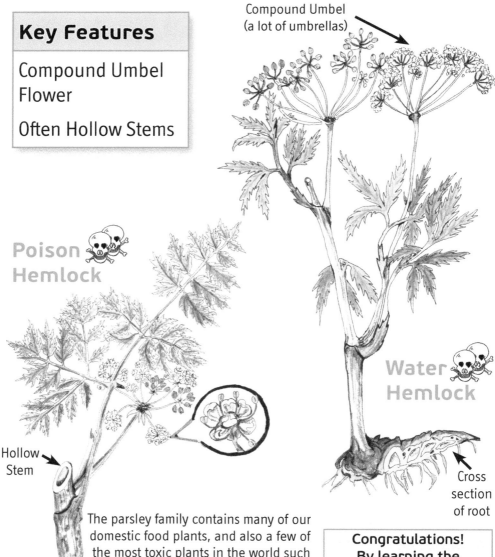

Compound Umbel
(a lot of umbrellas)

Key Features

Compound Umbel
Flower

Often Hollow Stems

Poison
Hemlock

Water
Hemlock

Hollow
Stem

Cross
section
of root

The parsley family contains many of our
domestic food plants, and also a few of
the most toxic plants in the world such
as Poison and Water hemlock.

Other members of the parsley family are: carrots, dill,
caraway, parsnips, biscuit roots, angelica, fennel, cumin, and cilantro.

**Congratulations!
By learning the
characteristics of
these six plant families,
you now know very
powerful information
about 29,000 plants!**

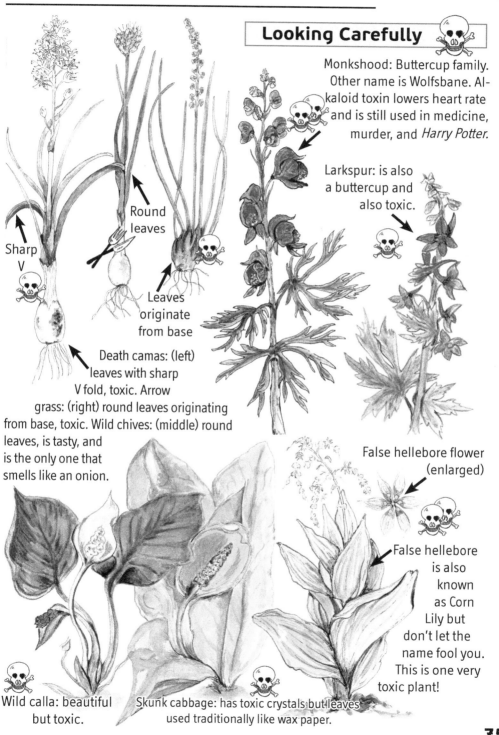

Looking Carefully

Monkshood: Buttercup family. Other name is Wolfsbane. Alkaloid toxin lowers heart rate and is still used in medicine, murder, and *Harry Potter.*

Larkspur: is also a buttercup and also toxic.

Round leaves

Sharp V

Leaves originate from base

Death camas: (left) leaves with sharp V fold, toxic. Arrow grass: (right) round leaves originating from base, toxic. Wild chives: (middle) round leaves, is tasty, and is the only one that smells like an onion.

False hellebore flower (enlarged)

False hellebore is also known as Corn Lily but don't let the name fool you. This is one very toxic plant!

Wild calla: beautiful but toxic.

Skunk cabbage: has toxic crystals but leaves used traditionally like wax paper.

Plants

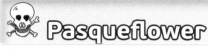 **Pasqueflower** *Anemone patens*

One of the first flowers up in spring. They can grow out of the snow!

The thick, fuzzy hairs and deep, dish-shaped flower collect solar rays and can raise the temperature by as much as 18 degrees F. Insects take advantage of this to survive.

All *Anemone* plants are toxic. They have big, fluffy seed heads that look like "Truffula Trees" from a Dr. Seuss book.

Key features: very large, purple to blue flower petals, extremely fuzzy all over, and few to no leaves.

BORAGE

 **Bluebells** *Mertensia sp.*

You can find several different species of bluebells in Alaska. All species are edible and easily identifiable.

Although all parts are edible, if you eat just the leaves, the flowers can help repopulate communities.

They are a healthy addition to many meals. Cooking can change flavor and ease of digestion.

Great source of vitamins and minerals otherwise missing in the average backcountry diet.

Key features: small, blue to purple, bell-shaped flowers in clumps, alternating, soft, smooth leaves that smell and taste faintly of oysters.

BORAGE

 **Harebell** *Campanula rotundifolia*

Loves cold places; it grows best in average temp below 32 F.

Leaves and flowers can be a tasty trail snack or pot herb. Harebell is one source of blue dye. Haida, native people of Southeast Alaska/ Pacific Northwest, called them "blue rain flowers"; they weren't picked because it would cause it to rain.

The roots can be boiled and eaten with a "nutlike" taste.

Key features: purple, bell-shaped flower, with large, three-pronged, white stigma, and thin, sparse leaves on narrow stem.

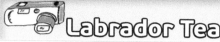

Labrador Tea
HEATH
Rhododendron groenlandicum

Caution with this small shrub! A tea of the leaves has a long history of being used as a medicinal tea or wash for treating pain, inflammation and Type 2 diabetes, as well as a daily tea by many northern peoples.

However, chemical analysis has shown that it contains some toxic compounds that, used too often or in large quantities, could be harmful. It is also very similar to Marsh Labrador tea (*Rhododendron tomentosumi*) which is reported to be more toxic and may not be safe as a tea.

Key features: woody stem, elliptical, leathery, evergreen leaves, and small white flowers in large clumps.

Sitka Burnet
ROSE
Sanguisorba canadensis

To see the rose family flower structure you will have to look closely! From a distance all you are seeing is the overly-large stamen that extends beyond the internal flower structure to help prevent self-pollination.

Leaves can be used to make tea, and can also be eaten after boiling to remove the bitter taste. Said to be a good addition to miso.

Key features: serrated leaves look opposite (but are actually alternate if you look very closely), with cone-like flower structure.

Yarrow
ASTER
Achillea millefolium

Common throughout the Northern Hemisphere.

Very safe, no poisonous look-a-likes. Very common in gardens, parks, and lawns. Can even be seen growing between the cracks in your local sidewalk.

Historically leaves were applied to wounds to stop bleeding. Some birds line their nests with yarrow to reduce parasites.

Makes a great tea from the fresh leaves! Use 2-6 leaves per cup and add spruce needles for variety.

Key features: ferny leaves that have herby, medicinal smell with tiny, white flowers in large, flat clumps.

Arctic Dock

BUCKWHEAT
Rumex arcticus

Like most dock species, the young leaves make a great lemon-flavored addition to meals. Recommend stripping the leaves from the center vein, boil for 2 min., then remove and chill to stop cooking process.

Some people like the young leaves as a salad green before they get too tough.

As with other dock and sorrel species, if you eat too much (especially raw), the oxalic acid could upset your stomach.

Key features: substantial, broad leaves with stiff, thick middle vein and tall, red flower stalk covered in papery, red seeds and should taste lemony.

Mountain Sorrel

BUCKWHEAT
Oxyria digyna

This plant likes growing in rocks. The heart-shaped leaves are high in vitamins and were used by Alaskan natives to prevent scurvy.

All above-ground parts are edible; it can be eaten raw in small quantities (< 20 leaves) and has great lemony flavor but should be cooked if you plan on eating more. Cooking breaks down the oxalic acid.

Another great way to enjoy this plant is use a few leaves and some sugar to make a tasty lemonade!

Key features: fleshy, heart-shaped leaves growing low to the ground, often in rock fields, torch-like flower spike, and very strong lemon flavor.

Roseroot

STONECROP
Rhodiola rosea

All above-ground parts of this succulent (fleshy) plant can be eaten cooked or raw. As with so many plants, the younger ones are better eating.

Roseroot has been compared in studies to anti-depressants. It performed much better than the placebo, not as well as the prescription, but it had fewer side effects.

In Chinese medicine, this plant is used to treat altitude sickness.

Key features: Only grows to several inches tall with very fleshy, small, pointed leaves and tiny red flowers on top like a hat.

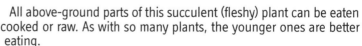

Snow Buttercup

BUTTERCUP
Ranunculus nivalis

Like all buttercups, these toxic, very waxy flowers look like plastic.

They need a snow depth of 6.5-10 feet in the winter to germinate, and can often be found growing right at the edge of a melting snow bank.

This plant is a heliotrope, "sun follower", growing unevenly from side-to-side to keep the flower always pointed toward the sun.

Key features: five, waxy yellow petals form a round flower-shape, with three to five lobes per waxy leaf and numerous stamen surrounding cone-like flower center.

Dryads

ROSE
Dryad species

Arctic dryads (left) and the more common White Mountain avens (right, with same basic, low, leathery leaf) form a dark carpet over the arctic landscape, especially in well-drained, cobbly soils.

These flowers have feathery "hairs" to help keep warm in their harsh habitat. The seed heads are spirals that unwind into white woolly tufts.

Key features: very dense carpet of leathery, dark green leaves with showy white or yellow flowers on tall stems poking up through the leaf mat.

Cinquefoil

ROSE
Potentilla sp.

Cinquefoils were used in "Witches Flying Ointment" and in love potions. It is currently used by herbalists as a skin wash (high tannins) and a red dye in the leather industry.

The flowers and leaves often look like those of strawberries, but without producing any fruit, giving cinquefoils the nickname "barren strawberry". Some cinquefoils, like Silverweed (*P. anserina*), were very important root crops for many native northwest peoples, and especially productive areas were "owned".

Key features: (cinque = five) five-petaled, yellow flowers with many showy yellow to orange stamen. Petals not waxy or stiff like buttercups.

Plants

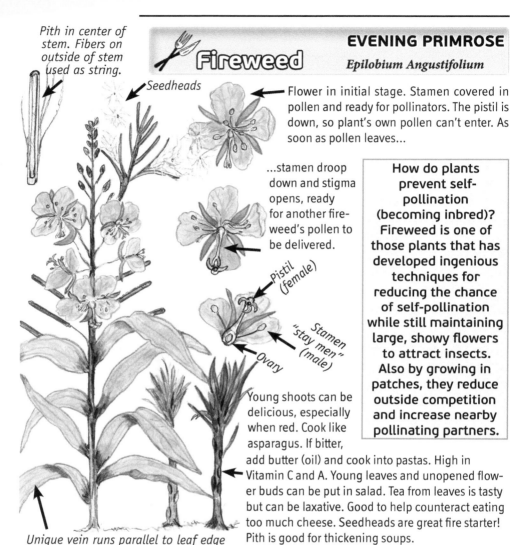

Pith in center of stem. Fibers on outside of stem used as string.

Seedheads

Fireweed

Flower in initial stage. Stamen covered in pollen and ready for pollinators. The pistil is down, so plant's own pollen can't enter. As soon as pollen leaves...

...stamen droop down and stigma opens, ready for another fireweed's pollen to be delivered.

Pistil (female)

Stamen "stay men" (male)

Ovary

How do plants prevent self-pollination (becoming inbred)? Fireweed is one of those plants that has developed ingenious techniques for reducing the chance of self-pollination while still maintaining large, showy flowers to attract insects. Also by growing in patches, they reduce outside competition and increase nearby pollinating partners.

Young shoots can be delicious, especially when red. Cook like asparagus. If bitter, add butter (oil) and cook into pastas. High in Vitamin C and A. Young leaves and unopened flower buds can be put in salad. Tea from leaves is tasty but can be laxative. Good to help counteract eating too much cheese. Seedheads are great fire starter! Pith is good for thickening soups.

Unique vein runs parallel to leaf edge

FROM THE BOTTOM UP

Fireweed matures from the bottom up. The flowers at the bottom of the plant have the stigma exposed and ready for pollen, but the flowers at the top only have pollen available. Fortunately, the hairy bees that are the plant's primary pollinators work from the bottom up, so they capture pollen from the top of one plant, then head to the bottom of next plant and spread that pollen into the open pistil ready to be fertilized. Cross-pollination at work! Close relative, River beauty, does not have this adaptation.

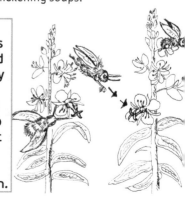

Wet Meadows

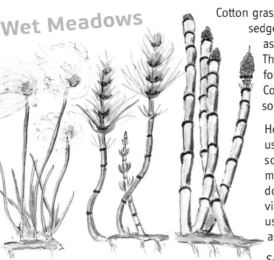

Cotton grass is not a grass at all! It is a water-loving sedge. You can guess your soil pH from this grass as it loves open peat bogs and acidic soils. The cotton-like seed heads have been used for paper, wound dressings and candle wicks. Cooked roots and stems have been a food source for many northern tribes.

Horsetails are living fossils! This plant family used to dominate the Paleozoic landscape; some horsetails were tree sized! Unlike more recent plant adaptations, horsetails do not have pollen; rather they reproduce via spores. The silica they contain can be used as sand paper, for scrubbing pots, or as light green dye.

Scouring rush is a distinctively jointed plant full of sharp silicone dioxide, making it ideal sandpaper for smoothing arrow shafts, canoes, utensils and scrubbing pots. The Tlingit used the roots for decorating baskets.

Cotton Grass	Horsetail	Scouring Rush
Eriophorum angustifolium	Equisetum sp.	Equisetum hyemale
SEDGE	HORSETAIL	HORSETAIL

Cushion Plants

How does being low to the ground help these plants survive in an arctic or alpine environment? Wind is as much of a problem for arctic plants as cold. By being low, they avoid the worst of the sharp, wind-driven ice crystals. Low plants also can trap their own dead leaves to use as insulation. These plants can also trap dust to get fresh soil. Many of the plants are hairy to help with warmth and water retention.

Low and Slow! Moss campion can be 350 years old, and the base may only be 2 feet in diameter.

Arctic Forget-Me-Not: Closely related to the Alaska state flower *Myosotis alpestris*—a taller version of this beautiful flower.

There are many saxifrage species in Alaska. Most have low leaves and grow on thin soil or even rock. The Latin word "Saxifraga" means "stone-breaker" because of its traditional use treating or "breaking" kidney stones, not because they break rocks!

Arctic Forget-me-not	Moss Campion	Saxifrage
Eritrichium nanum	Silene acaulis	Saxifrage sp.
BORAGE	PINK	SAXIFRAGE

Plants

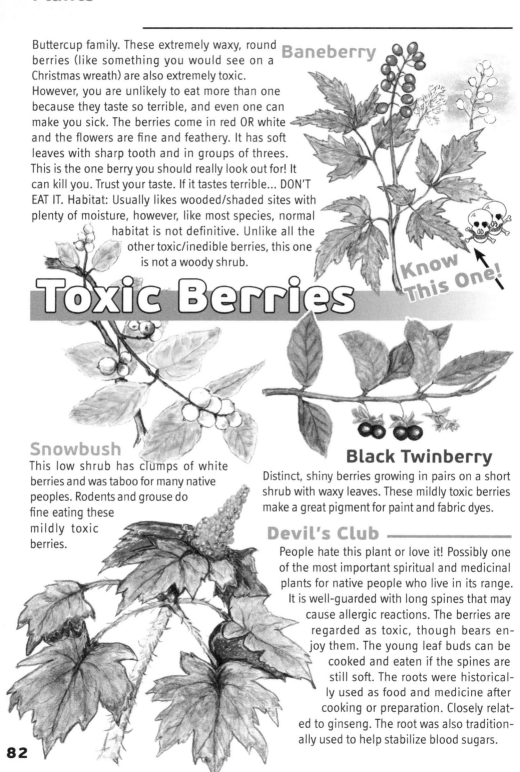

Buttercup family. These extremely waxy, round berries (like something you would see on a Christmas wreath) are also extremely toxic. However, you are unlikely to eat more than one because they taste so terrible, and even one can make you sick. The berries come in red OR white and the flowers are fine and feathery. It has soft leaves with sharp tooth and in groups of threes. This is the one berry you should really look out for! It can kill you. Trust your taste. If it tastes terrible... DON'T EAT IT. Habitat: Usually likes wooded/shaded sites with plenty of moisture, however, like most species, normal habitat is not definitive. Unlike all the other toxic/inedible berries, this one is not a woody shrub.

Baneberry

Know This One!

Toxic Berries

Snowbush

This low shrub has clumps of white berries and was taboo for many native peoples. Rodents and grouse do fine eating these mildly toxic berries.

Black Twinberry

Distinct, shiny berries growing in pairs on a short shrub with waxy leaves. These mildly toxic berries make a great pigment for paint and fabric dyes.

Devil's Club

People hate this plant or love it! Possibly one of the most important spiritual and medicinal plants for native people who live in its range. It is well-guarded with long spines that may cause allergic reactions. The berries are regarded as toxic, though bears enjoy them. The young leaf buds can be cooked and eaten if the spines are still soft. The roots were historically used as food and medicine after cooking or preparation. Closely related to ginseng. The root was also traditionally used to help stabilize blood sugars.

Almost Inedible

Red Osier Dogwood

Stream-side shrub with bright red bark. The leaves are smooth (no tooth) and shiny. The berries are pink-ish purple to white and extremely unpalatable. The leaf veins contain a latex-like substance, which stretches out in long white lines when torn. Extremely important winter browse for moose. Habitat: stream-side.

Red Elderberry

Very tiny red berries in large clumps. Leaves are opposite and "pinnately compound"(usually in groups of six).
Berries can be fermented into wine or eaten after cooking to make them edible. They make a tangy jelly. Branches from this medium-large shrub were used for friction fires, but all parts of the plant except berries contain cyanide. Habitat: usually found in moist clearings and open forests.

Mountain Ash

Berries also grow in large clumps, but individual berries are much larger than elderberries, and are either red or orange when ripe. The leaves of this small to medium-size shrub are heavily toothed, and although they appear opposite each other, they are actually alternate. Birds, especially waxwings and grosbeaks, love and rely on these berries to survive. Habitat: usually in open coniferous forests and at meadow edges and rockslide clearings.

Soapberry

The name says it all. These berries taste like soap! Great for a prank, also good for making into a wash to shampoo hair.
Native peoples used to whip these berries up (possibly using split willow branches like a whisk) to make a frothy substance into which lots of sweet berries were added and the whole thing was eaten as a dessert. Medium-sized shrub with white "speckles" covering the berries, bark and leaves (which are small and oval).
Habitat: usually relatively dry sites.

Tasty Berries

Alaska has an astounding number of edible berries! If you have learned the one you really cannot eat (Baneberry) and the other ones you don't really want to eat because they might make you sick, then it is time to trust your taste buds. **Salmonberry** is a large shrub with raspberry-like fruits from red to yellow. We personally like the yellow flavor the best. **Saskatoon** is another tall shrub with berries that ripen at different times within the clump.

Blueberry species in Alaska are numerous and sometimes hard to tell apart. Fortunately, all the different species of blueberry and huckleberry have very similar looking fruit (from blue to black) and all are tasty. **Cloudberry** is a very short plant with a few yellow berries per plant and can be delicious. The immature fruit is red; the mature fruit is yellow.

Lingonberries, also known as Low Bush cranberries, are like a cranberry but sweeter.

Bog cranberry plants are tiny, but the red, sweet fruits are large.

Bearberry, or Kinnikinik, is a mealy, red berry that overwinters and is a key food for bears and other animals in the spring. The **Red Currant** is like other currants in that the dead flower is attached to the bottom of these tangy, juicy berries, which can become sweeter after the first frost.

Saskatoon

Salmonberry

Blueberry species

Red Currant

Cloudberry

Bog Cranberry

Bearberry

Lingonberry

Tasty Berries

Two lilies that like to grow along stream banks and under forest canopy are **False Solomon Seal** and **Twisted Stalk**. False solomon seal has clumps of feathery white flowers and the leaves don't clasp the stem as much as Twisted stalk. Also, Twisted stalk grows in a spiral with berries and flowers coming off at intervals, not in clumps at the very end. Solomon seal berries are usually only tasty after the first frost. **Bunchberry** has a very distinctive whorled pattern and berries in a "bunch". The berries are tasty but pulpy. **Crowberry,** unlike all the other berries on this page which prefer tree canopy, grows in low, exposed sites from sea level bogs to alpine tundra. Some people like the berries, some not so much. Leaves look a lot like Mountain heather when not in fruit. There are more edible berries than the ones listed here. Most are similar to raspberries.

Food For Thought

Have you ever eaten too many cherries from the grocery store? Yup. That can happen with wild berries as well. Even if they taste amazing, remember over-eating is over-eating no matter how cultivated or wild the fruit is.

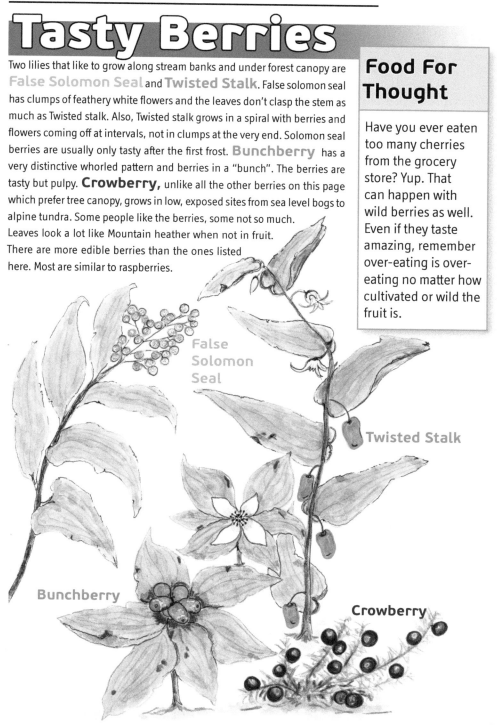

False Solomon Seal

Twisted Stalk

Bunchberry

Crowberry

Field I.D.

You just found a monkeyflower...you think... maybe? It looks kinda like a monkeyflower, but the illustration isn't THAT great, so now what? You know they're edible, and when cooked, can be quite tasty and salty. You'd love some fresh greens with your dinner. You're pretty sure, but here's what we do when we're almost confident but need to make sure you stay safe.

Starting Point:

- We are 100% sure it is not one of the deadliest of the deadlies! No Water or Poison hemlock, (it's not a parsley family), False hellebore (which has only parallel veins like a lily), or monkshood, or baneberry.

- We are also 100% sure it is not an Iris, Death camas, or larkspur. BUT it could be a buttercup. We haven't seen a flower yet for positive identification, so now there's a yellow warning flag.

- Does the habitat work for either monkeyflower or buttercup? Yes, it was near a spring, which both species like. Second yellow flag. But we're still curious.

- We are stuck without finding a flower. So we go searching...

That's a monkeyflower flower! We pick a leaf from the plant in flower, and carry it back to the un-flowering plant for careful comparison. They match. We are 100% confident on our identification.

- We do a taste test of a very small amount and decide it tastes good. Then we pick a moderate amount of young, tender leaves, sauté them briefly, and enjoy a field dinner rich in vitamins and minerals.

- We take a picture of the plant for future reference, note the picture number in our journal, and if we have time, sketch it. When we get back to civilization, we consult a field guide or talk to an expert to learn more.

The Fungus Among us

Boletes, like this edible King bolete, do not have linear gills. Instead, they are often identified by having tubes.

If you cut boletes in half, you can see a cross-section of the spore tubes.

NEVER eat mushrooms without input from an expert. They are VERY difficult to correctly identify!

Beach Lovers

Beach greens, *Honckenya peploides*, has several other names such as Sea chickweed or Seabeach sandwort. This plant is a member of the Pink family. It is a fleshy, short plant with clasping leaves that grows in clumps in the sand. Flowers are white, five-petaled, with five long stamens. This plant is very tasty!

Beach pea, *Lathyrus japonicus*, is one of the few edible peas (but should not comprise more than 30 percent of your diet). The leaves are large, elliptical and pinnately compound. The pea pods are only tasty when young, otherwise they are bitter and tough. They are best steamed or sautéed.

Beach Greens

Beach Pea

Take a Lichen to it!

Plant growth in Alaska is limited by many things, one of the most important being summer warmth. Plants can only photosynthesize when they reach a certain temperature. In addition, the thin top soil and permafrost limits root growth. These conditions favor hardy, short species who don't require much soil.

Reindeer lichen is tall for a lichen but short for a plant, and appears fuzzy from its branching structure.

Researchers studying lichen recovery after tundra fires found reindeer lichen had not regenerated well after 14 years, while shrubs and other vascular plants had come back at higher rates than before. These, and other studies about the effects of global warming and the increase of tundra fires, pose interesting and disturbing questions about the abundance of reindeer lichen in the future. Without these crucial winter lichens, will grazing caribou herds switch to eating shrubs and other plants favored by warmer summers? Or will there be not enough forage during the winter months for the huge herds of wandering caribou?

Primary Types of Lichen:

Crustose

These lichens are "crusty", small, low-growing, and without a lower cortex, which means they cannot be removed without damaging the organism. These are commonly clinging to rocks and soil.

Foliose

These lichens look like they have foliage (or leaves). They have a lower cortex, which means they can be removed and applied to hummingbird nests and continue growing.

Fruticose

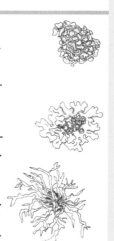

These lichens look like they have large, dangling fruiting bodies. They often drape down from trees, or cover the tundra like "Reindeer lichen", a primary winter forage for caribou.

Lichen Structure

Algae takes nitrogen gas from the air and turns it into biologically usable compounds (food). This means lichens with cyanobacteria, or blue-green algae, can be major contributors to soil fertility, especially in the arctic. Lichens are thought to be among the oldest living things on earth.

Upper cortex made of fungal tissue and embedded yeast. Protective layer for lichen .

Fungal hyphae and algal cells (cyanobacteria or blue-green algae or both).

Lower cortex. Not present in crustose.

Reproductive Unit

Algal Cell

Fungal Hyphae

Lichens can remain active at freezing temperatures because of the alcohols they contain. They also can survive extreme heat, around 150 degrees F, which can be a real issue living on a south-facing, black rock. They can photosynthesize under snow, where there is moisture and a tiny bit of sunlight. Lichens have survived three of the past five mass extinctions, so their survival strategy seems to be effective.

Lungwort lichens grow abundantly in the conifer canopy, and squeeze between reindeer lichen on the tundra.

The Cladonia species produces a two-part growth form. The underlying mat of lichen is relatively flat, while the fruiting twigs look like pixie cups or golf tees.

Or a Moss

Mosses often appear spiny and are always short. Like ferns, they are spore-bearing, but unlike ferns they lack vessels to easily transport water and nutrients, limiting their size. They pass water though their leaf surface almost instantly, meaning they can appear dried out and dead one minute, but add a little water and they are suddenly revived. In a cold climate, this means they can move water out to their leaf surface immediately and keep dangerous ice crystals away from their insides.

Bugged

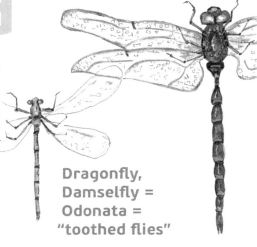

**Dragonfly,
Damselfly =
Odonata =
"toothed flies"**

Insect Orders

Although some of these examples, like the Monarch butterfly (bright orange) are rare in Alaska (there's one recorded specimen), insect diversity even in cold climates is astounding. Insects are so complex and tricky to examine, learning them by species or even family is difficult. Instead, many scientists and naturalists use "Orders," which have broad characteristics that apply to most members.

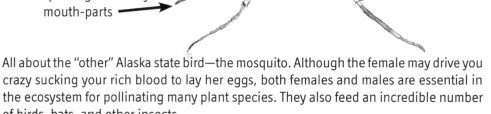

The smaller male mosquito does not bite, but collects pollen with these fuzzy mouth-parts. ➡

The larger female mosquito needs rich blood to produce eggs, so she has the sharp biting (and itchy) mouth-parts ➡

All about the "other" Alaska state bird—the mosquito. Although the female may drive you crazy sucking your rich blood to lay her eggs, both females and males are essential in the ecosystem for pollinating many plant species. They also feed an incredible number of birds, bats, and other insects.

When the female is ready to lay eggs, she picks a pond, or shallow pool and lays her eggs above the water, but below the high-water line. The eggs then winter under the snow, waiting until the spring melt to become submerged in water and hatch for their new life as larvae, then pupae, then the winged menace. Some arctic species have adapted to be able to lay a few eggs using only the food stores they collected as larvae. Some females hibernate over winter.

By Cool Bugs

Inupiat (Northern Native Alaskan) word for mosquito is "Kiktugiak".

Butterfly, Moth = Lepidoptera = "Scaly wings"

Flies and Mosquitoes = Diptera = "two wings"

Ants, bees, wasps = Hymenoptera = "membrane wings" (Ants lost their wings)

Cicadas, Leaf Hoppers = Hemiptera and Homoptera = "half wings"

Beetles = Coleoptera = "hard wing"

91

Why So Dark?

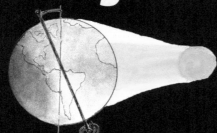

Why the long winter?
Imagine the earth spinning on the north/south axis like a top (tipped at 23.4º). Each of these images represents a day, and each image would rotate 360 degrees in approximately 24 hours. Follow the arrows.

In the northern winter, the planet is tilted away from the sun, meaning only low-angle, diffuse light reaches the northern latitudes.

March Equinox 20/21

Red Circle = Arctic Circle

Spring

Winter

June Solstice 21/22

Dec. Solstice 21/22

Summer

Fall

Sept. Equinox 20/21

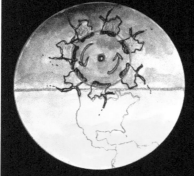

Closer look at December Solstice

On the shortest day of the year in Alaska, part of the state is above the Arctic Circle and doesn't see any sunlight at all! The sky gets a lighter shade of gray as the planet rotates toward the sun, but actual beams of sunlight never make it around the curvature of the Earth.

Northern Lights

This fantastic light show is a highlight of arctic winter. But why? Is it just the long dark that allows one to see the magic dancing greens and pinks through the sky? No. Although the dark helps make sure the light show is spectacularly visible whenever it happens, it is actually the earth's magnetic field and a bunch of very excited ions that makes for such a magical sky show in both summer and winter.

Aluttiq word for Northern Lights is "quigyat"

When excited ions and electrons interact with oxygen they produce red light high up, and green light closer to the surface. When they interact with nitrogen, they produce purple light, then blue lower down.

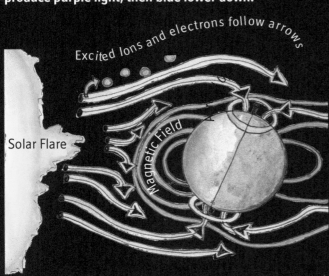

Excited Ions and electrons follow arrows

Magnetic Field

Solar Flare

Solar flares excite ions and electrons, which head toward earth but are pulled by the magnetic field toward both poles (North and South). The place where these excited ions and electrons enter the atmosphere is known as the Auroral Oval. As the excited ions/electrons interact with oxygen and nitrogen, they slow down, releasing their energy as light.

Surviving the long dark winter

Snoozing Mamma. **Brown bear**: When to have young.

Spitballing **Gray jay**: How to store food above snow.

Little Brown bat hangin' by a toe: Where to stay warmer but still hibernate.

Supercool squirrel. **Arctic ground squirrel**: Making body fluids below freezing.

Frog-cicle! **Wood frog**: How to freeze and survive it.

Many creatures in Alaska avoid the long winter months by migrating south. For those that stay, the very short, productive summer is over, and now the long winter must be survived. For some creatures, this is a time to shutdown, and for others, this is the season of endurance and ingenuity.

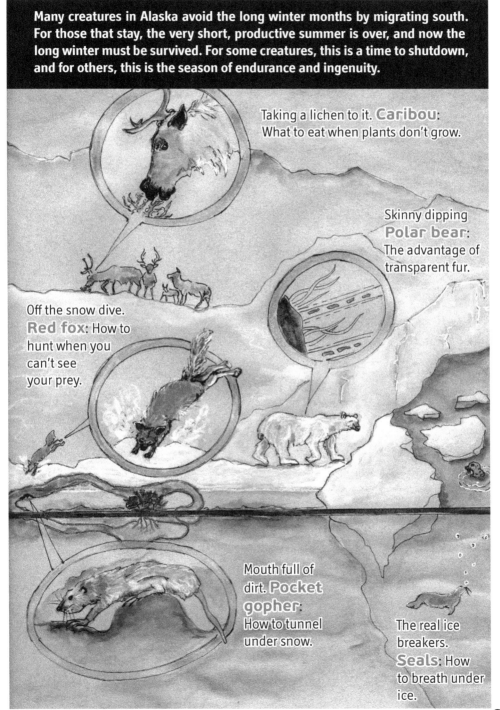

Taking a lichen to it. **Caribou**: What to eat when plants don't grow.

Skinny dipping **Polar bear**: The advantage of transparent fur.

Off the snow dive. **Red fox**: How to hunt when you can't see your prey.

Mouth full of dirt. **Pocket gopher**: How to tunnel under snow.

The real ice breakers. **Seals**: How to breath under ice.

Winter

Brown bears find remote dens to hibernate in. If a female has enough fat reserves going into winter, she will have her cubs. They weigh around a pound when born, and suckle on the dozing mother until big enough to emerge in spring.

Gray jays survive winter by sticking food above the snow-line in special spitballs.

Little Brown bats spend winter hanging by their toes from the ceiling of caves, in a state of near shutdown. Caves remain warm enough to keep them alive.

White Nose Syndrome

White Nose is a fungal infection that likes cold and causes bats to become dehydrated or acidified. In the later stages, it shows up as white spots on bats' noses and wings. It causes hibernating bats to wake up more often, which results in depletion of the necessary fat reserves and ultimately starvation. The fungus is spread from bat-to-bat, and by human cavers. Millions of bats are dying of this introduced disease. Thankfully, White Nose has not been seen in Alaska yet.

Arctic ground squirrels super cool their body fluids. They have the coldest body temp. recorded in any mammal (-3 C or 27F). They double their body weight before hibernation, which is nine months of their year. Their amazing ability to survive cold may hold the key to better organ transplants and future cryogenics.

Wood frogs freeze! However, they minimize the damage of sharp ice crystals forming in their bodies in a number of ways. They super concentrate cryoprotectans (freeze protectors) in their delicate cells to drive out water. Then they use agents (like dust or bacteria) to grow ice crystals in their bodies away from cell walls and vital organs.

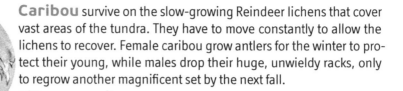

Caribou survive on the slow-growing Reindeer lichens that cover vast areas of the tundra. They have to move constantly to allow the lichens to recover. Female caribou grow antlers for the winter to protect their young, while males drop their huge, unwieldy racks, only to regrow another magnificent set by the next fall.

Polar bear hair is clear, while their skin is black! They look white because that is the color not absorbed by the hairs, but reflected back. This means the black skin can warm in the sun, but the reflected white also helps prevent sunburn. The guard hairs are full of air pockets, which help insulate the bears, along with a dense undercoat.

Seals and other marine mammals don't have gills, so must surface to breath. This can be difficult when your ocean habitat is covered in winter ice. These mammals create breathing holes by keeping the water disturbed enough it doesn't freeze. This is also where polar bears will go to hunt. The loss of continuous sea ice threatens the bears ability to make it to seal breathing holes to survive, since these bears don't hibernate

Red foxes and other small mammal hunters (like owls) rely on a constant supply of invisible prey. They use their ears to triangulate the position of rodents scurrying under the snow, and with a sudden spring, plunge head first (or in the owl's case, talons first) into the deep snow for a mousy meal.

Pocket gophers and other tunneling mammals are the great rototillers, moving and aerating huge amounts of soil, which helps in soil health and plant growth. In the winter, they bring long lines of excavated soil up into the snow, or the subnivean space, to get it out of their way. After the spring snow-melt, these long lines of exposed soil, or eskers, look like inverted tunnels sitting on top of grass or even bushes.

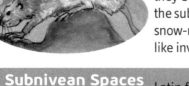

Subnivean Spaces Latin for Sub=under Nivean=snow. There is a lot of warm, insulating airspace in snow. When it piles up on the relatively stable, warm earth, the nearest layers of snow melt and form an ice roof, beneath which many small mammals travel, eat, and stay relatively safe.

Learn More
(and some of our references)

This book is designed to be taken with you. It's just a starting point. We hope it makes you want to learn more! Here are some of our favorites. If you only buy one book, get *Natural History of the Pacific Northwest Mountains* by **Daniel Mathews**. Although he is missing a few key Alaska/arctic species, he covers everything from geology to bugs and his information is fascinating!

General Natural History:
E.C. Pielou's *A Naturalist's Guide to the Arctic*

Birds: David Allen Sibley's bird guide is great, but the phone App has the added benefit of multiple songs for each bird.

John Young's *What the Robin Knows* is amazing for bird language.

Allaboutbirds.org Cornell Bird Lab Online

Plants: *Plants of the Pacific Northwest Coast* by Pojar and Mackinnon

Tomas J. Elpel's *Botany In A Day*

Edible and Medicinal Plants:
Beverly Gray's *The Boreal Herbal*

Tomas J. Elpel and Kris Reed *Foraging The Mountain West*

Tracking: James C. Lowery's *The Tracker's Field Guide*

Mark Elbroch's *Mammal Tracks and Sign*

Natural Journaling and Drawing: John Muir Laws' book *The Laws Guide to Nature Drawing and Journaling*. His website has great free tutorials. johnmuirlaws.com

Doug Lindstrand's *Alaska Sketchbook*

Mammals: Peterson Field Guides to *Mammals of North America*

Alaska Department of Fish and Game: adfg.alaska.gov

Cool Current Science:

Subscribe to **Science News**. They distill the most current research into interesting and fun articles.

Marine:

Susan c. Byersdorfer and Leslie J. Watson's *Common Marine Fishes and Invertebrates of Alaska*

There are many people who made this book possible!

Without Ashley Wise there would never have been an Alaska booklet. Filip Sanna was a wealth of information, edited, and answered endless questions. Shannon Rochelle provided us wonderful plant lists. Glenn Goodrich is not only guilty of hiring us many years ago, but also for providing information about the creatures in the ocean. Levi Old helped with overall content and Joe Frost and Marianna Young are meticulous editors. Jim Culver sent us further down the path to naturalists by hiring us as such. David Allen Sibley, Keith Hansen, and John Young inspired us to always look and ask questions. John Muir Laws reminded us why we draw, and taught us how to have more fun doing it. To Jane Wohl and Barry Wohl, for inspiring a love of the natural world. And especially to Kathy and Aaron Mann who truly made this possible with all their support.

Do More:

NOLS

Teaching wilderness skills, medicine, and leadership.
NOLS is a nonprofit global wilderness school that seeks to help you step forward boldly as a leader.
www.NOLS.edu

Adventure Scientists

Explore Collect Protect
Adventure Scientists volunteers explore the planet while making a difference. They collect data to protect critical species and ecosystems

Adventurescientists.org

The Nature Conservancy

To conserve the lands and waters on which all life depends. Working around the world in 72 countries.

www.nature.org

Other Books by Sastrugi Press

2024 Total Eclipse State Series by Aaron Linsdau

Sastrugi Press has published state-specific guides for the 2024 total eclipse crossing over the United States. Check the Sastrugi Press website for the available state eclipse books: www.sastrugipress.com/eclipse

50 Wildlife Hotspots by Moose Henderson

Find out where to find animals and photograph them in Grand Teton National Park from a professional wildlife photographer. This unique guide shares the secret locations with the best chance at spotting wildlife.

Adventure Expedition One by Aaron Linsdau and Terry Williams M.D.

How do you set off on your first epic expedition? Where should you even start? This book has practical advice to help you begin planning your first trek. Dreaming, planning, training, doing, and returning alive are all covered in this guide.

Antarctic Tears by Aaron Linsdau

What would make someone give up a high-paying career to ski alone across Antarctica to the South Pole? This inspirational true story will make readers both cheer and cry. Fighting skin-freezing temperatures, infections, and emotional breakdown, Aaron Linsdau exposes the harsh realities of the world's largest wilderness. Discover what drives someone to the brink of destruction to pursue a dream.

Cache Creek by Susan Marsh

Five minutes from the hubbub of Jackson's town square, Cache Creek offers the chance for hikers to immerse themselves in wild nature. It is a popular hiking, biking, and cross-country ski area on the outskirts of Jackson, Wyoming.

Lost at Windy Corner by Aaron Linsdau

Windy Corner on Denali has claimed lives, fingers, and toes. What would make someone brave lethal weather, crevasses, and slick ice to attempt to summit North America's highest mountain? The author shares the lessons Denali teaches on managing goals and risks. Apply the message to build resilience and overcome adversity.

Voices at Twilight by Lori Howe, Ph.D.

Voices at Twilight is a guide that takes readers on a visual tour of twelve past and present Wyoming ghost towns. Contained within are travel directions, GPS coordinates, and tips for intrepid readers.www.sastrugipress.com

Visit Sastrugi Press on the web at www.sastrugipress.com to purchase the above titles in bulk. They are also available from your local bookstore or online retailers in print, e-book, or audiobook form. Thank you for choosing Sastrugi Press.

www.sastrugipress.com
"Turn the Page Loose"

CPSIA information can be obtained
at www.ICGtesting.com
Printed in the USA
BVHW021748160519
548506BV00019B/295/P